Introduction

The Science Coordination Group was set up with the aim of producing
specialised revision material for National Curriculum Science.
This is one of a set of six Workbooks which provide a full course of
tailor-made questions ideally suited to all the main Exam Board syllabuses for
GCSE Double Science.

These Workbooks have been produced to complement the popular range of
Revision Guides produced by the Science Coordination Group for GCSE
Double Science.

Throughout these books there is constant emphasis on the inescapable
need to ***keep learning the basic facts***. This simple message is hammered home
without compromise and without remorse, and whilst this traditionally brutal
philosophy may not be quite in line with some other approaches to education,
we still rather like it.   But only because it works.

Periodic Table

You should be pretty familiar with the 34 elements shown shaded.

You don't really need to know anything about the others.

Periods

Group O

| Group | I | II | | | | | | | | | | | | III | IV | V | VI | VII | |

1

| | | | | | | | | | | | | | | | | | | 1 |
| | | | | | | | | | | | | | | | | | | H Hydrogen 1 |

| | | | | | | | | | | | | | | | | | | 4 He Helium 2 |

Mass number →
Atomic number →

| 7 Li Lithium 3 | 9 Be Beryllium 4 | | | | | | | | | | | | 11 B Boron 5 | 12 C Carbon 6 | 14 N Nitrogen 7 | 16 O Oxygen 8 | 19 F Fluorine 9 | 20 Ne Neon 10 |

2

| 23 Na Sodium 11 | 24 Mg Magnesium 12 | | | | | | | | | | | | 27 Al Aluminium 13 | 28 Si Silicon 14 | 31 P Phosphorus 15 | 32 S Sulphur 16 | 35.5 Cl Chlorine 17 | 40 Ar Argon 18 |

3

| 39 K Potassium 19 | 40 Ca Calcium 20 | 45 Sc Scandium 21 | 48 Ti Titanium 22 | 51 V Vanadium 23 | 52 Cr Chromium 24 | 55 Mn Manganese 25 | 56 Fe Iron 26 | 59 Co Cobalt 27 | 59 Ni Nickel 28 | 64 Cu Copper 29 | 65 Zn Zinc 30 | 70 Ga Gallium 31 | 73 Ge Germanium 32 | 75 As Arsenic 33 | 79 Se Selenium 34 | 80 Br Bromine 35 | 84 Kr Krypton 36 |

4

| 85.5 Rb Rubidium 37 | 88 Sr Strontium 38 | 89 Y Yttrium 39 | 91 Zr Zirconium 40 | 93 Nb Niobium 41 | 96 Mo Molybdenum 42 | 98 Tc Technetium 43 | 101 Ru Ruthenium 44 | 103 Rh Rhodium 45 | 106 Pd Palladium 46 | 108 Ag Silver 47 | 112 Cd Cadmium 48 | 115 In Indium 49 | 119 Sn Tin 50 | 122 Sb Antimony 51 | 128 Te Tellurium 52 | 127 I Iodine 53 | 131 Xe Xenon 54 |

5

| 133 Cs Caesium 55 | 137 Ba Barium 56 | 139 La Lanthanum 57 | 178.5 Hf Hafnium 72 | 181 Ta Tantalum 73 | 184 W Tungsten 74 | 186 Re Rhenium 75 | 190 Os Osmium 76 | 192 Ir Iridium 77 | 195 Pt Platinum 78 | 197 Au Gold 79 | 201 Hg Mercury 80 | 204 Tl Thallium 81 | 207 Pb Lead 82 | 209 Bi Bismuth 83 | 210 Po Polonium 84 | 210 At Astatine 85 | 222 Rn Radon 86 |

6

| 223 Fr Francium 87 | 226 Ra Radium 88 | 227 Ac Actinium 89 |

7

The Lanthanides

| 140 Ce Cerium 58 | 141 Pr Praseodymium 59 | 144 Nd Neodymium 60 | 147 Pm Promethium 61 | 150 Sm Samarium 62 | 152 Eu Europium 63 | 157 Gd Gadolinium 64 | 159 Tb Terbium 65 | 162 Dy Dysprosium 66 | 165 Ho Holmium 67 | 167 Er Erbium 68 | 169 Tm Thulium 69 | 173 Yb Ytterbium 70 | 175 Lu Lutetium 71 |

The Actinides

| 232 Th Thorium 90 | 231 Pa Protactinium 91 | 238 U Uranium 92 | 237 Np Neptunium 93 | 242 Pu Plutonium 94 | 243 Am Americium 95 | 247 Cm Curium 96 | 247 Bk Berkelium 97 | 251 Cf Californium 98 | 254 Es Einsteinium 99 | 253 Fm Fermium 100 | 256 Md Mendelevium 101 the old rogue | 254 No Nobelium 102 | 257 Lr Lawrencium 103 |

The Most Basic Stuff of all — you must learn your elements

1) *Chemistry* is all about *knowing the differences* between the various elements and compounds.

2) And one thing's for sure — if you don't know the really *basic* information about all the elements that you come across, then you've no chance of sorting anything else out.

3) This page has the *really basic stuff* on.

4) The *position* of each element in the *Periodic Table* determines the whole of its *chemical behaviour*.

5) *At the very least* you must know where all the 34 shaded ones are.

6) You must also learn the *Reactivity Series for Metals* shown below and *all the common ions* too.

7) Practise all three regularly by covering up parts of the tables and trying to remember what goes where.

The Reactivity Series of Metals

1) **Potassium**
2) **Sodium**
3) **Calcium**
4) **Magnesium**
5) **Aluminium**
   (Carbon)
6) **Zinc**
7) **Iron**
8) **Lead**
   (Hydrogen)
9) **Copper**
10) **Silver**
11) **Gold**
12) **Platinum**

Common Ions You Really Should Know

1⁺ ions	2⁺ ions	3⁺ ions	4⁺/4⁻	3⁻	2⁻ ions	1⁻ ions
Li^+ (lithium)	Mg^{2+} (magnesium)	Al^{3+} (aluminium)	Very rare	Fairly rare	O^{2-} (oxide)	F^- (fluoride)
Na^+ (sodium)	Ca^{2+} (calcium)	Fe^{3+} (iron(III))			S^{2-} (sulphide)	Cl^- (chloride)
K^+ (potassium)	Ba^{2+} (barium)	Cr^{3+} (chromium(III))				Br^- (bromide)
Cu^+ (copper(I))	Cu^{2+} (copper(II))					I^- (iodide)
Ag^+ (silver)	Fe^{2+} (iron(II))					NO_3^- (nitrate)
H^+ (hydrogen)	Zn^{2+} (zinc)	*Note that copper and iron can both form two different ions.*			SO_4^{2-} (sulphate)	OH^- (hydroxide)
NH_4^+ (ammonium)	Pb^{2+} (lead)				CO_3^{2-} (carbonate)	HCO_3^- (hydrogencarbonate)
These atoms lose **one** electron to form 1⁺ ions. (NH_4^+ is not an atom of course)	These atoms lose *two* electrons to form 2⁺ ions	These atoms lose *three* electrons to form 3⁺ ions	Atoms have a devil of a job gaining or losing three or four electrons.		These atoms/ molecules gain *two* electrons to form 2⁻ ions	These atoms/ molecules gain *one* electron to form 1⁻ ions

Contents

Published by Coordination Group Publications
Typesetting and layout by The Science Coordination Group

Coordinated by Paddy Gannon BSc MA

Printed by Hindson Print, Newcastle upon Tyne.

In the Laboratory

Common Laboratory Apparatus

1) The items of apparatus below are drawn in three dimensions. _Draw_ a _two dimensional_ picture of each item to its right, then _give its name_ and state its _uses_.

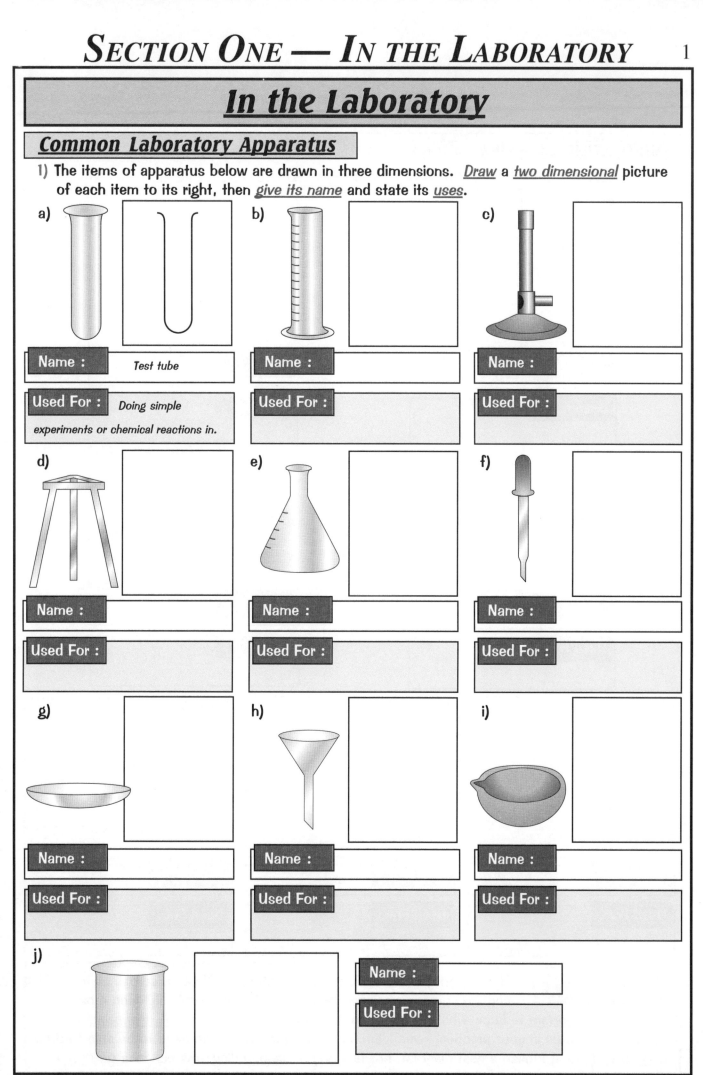

a)

Name : *Test tube*

Used For : *Doing simple experiments or chemical reactions in.*

b)

Name :

Used For :

c)

Name :

Used For :

d)

Name :

Used For :

e)

Name :

Used For :

f)

Name :

Used For :

g)

Name :

Used For :

h)

Name :

Used For :

i)

Name :

Used For :

j)

Name :

Used For :

In the Laboratory

Some More Common Laboratory Apparatus

2) Again _draw_ the apparatus next to each drawing, then _name it_ and _give its use_ in the laboratory.

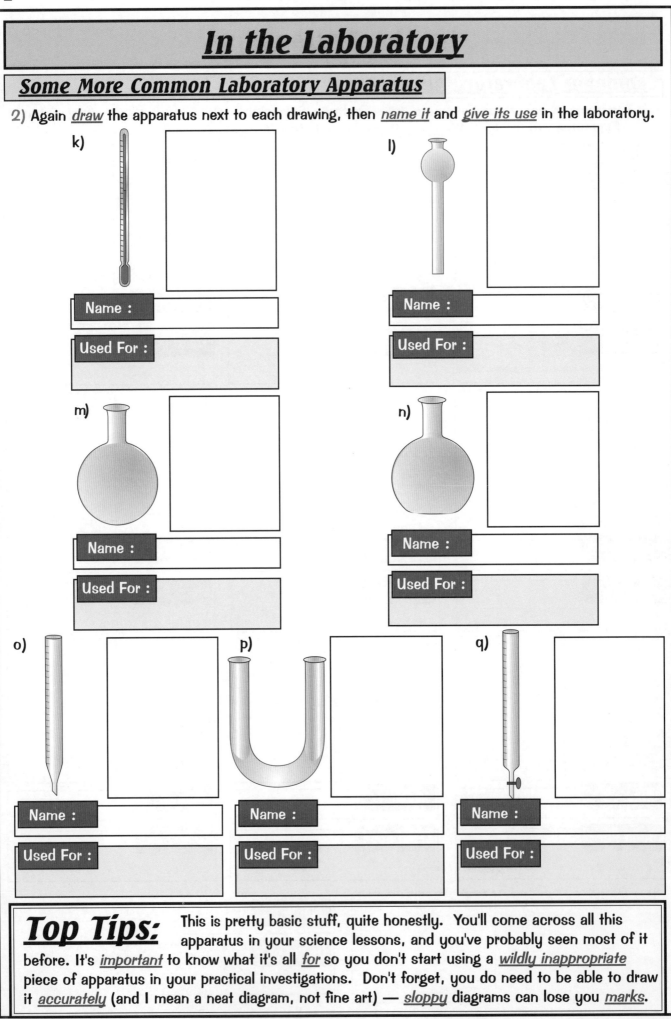

k)

Name :

Used For :

l)

Name :

Used For :

m)

Name :

Used For :

n)

Name :

Used For :

o)

Name :

Used For :

p)

Name :

Used For :

q)

Name :

Used For :

Top Tips: This is pretty basic stuff, quite honestly. You'll come across all this apparatus in your science lessons, and you've probably seen most of it before. It's _important_ to know what it's all _for_ so you don't start using a _wildly inappropriate_ piece of apparatus in your practical investigations. Don't forget, you do need to be able to draw it _accurately_ (and I mean a neat diagram, not fine art) — _sloppy_ diagrams can lose you _marks_.

Units

Measurement Units and Symbols

1) *Link up* the correct unit and symbol with the measurements below.

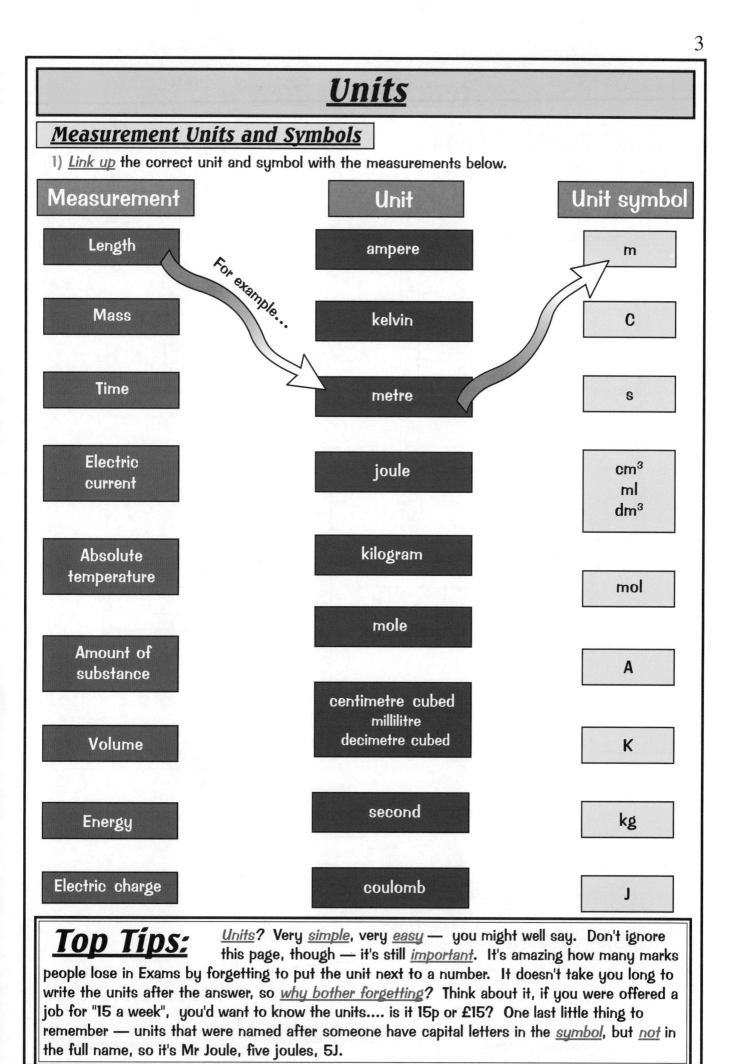

Measurement	Unit	Unit symbol
Length	ampere	m
Mass	kelvin	C
Time	metre	s
Electric current	joule	cm³ ml dm³
Absolute temperature	kilogram	mol
Amount of substance	mole	A
Volume	centimetre cubed millilitre decimetre cubed	K
Energy	second	kg
Electric charge	coulomb	J

Top Tips: *Units?* Very *simple*, very *easy* — you might well say. Don't ignore this page, though — it's still *important*. It's amazing how many marks people lose in Exams by forgetting to put the unit next to a number. It doesn't take you long to write the units after the answer, so *why bother forgetting*? Think about it, if you were offered a job for "15 a week", you'd want to know the units.... is it 15p or £15? One last little thing to remember — units that were named after someone have capital letters in the *symbol*, but *not* in the full name, so it's Mr Joule, five joules, 5J.

Reading Scales

Practice at Reading Scales

1) <u>Write</u> the measurements, including units where necessary, on the scales in the spaces provided:

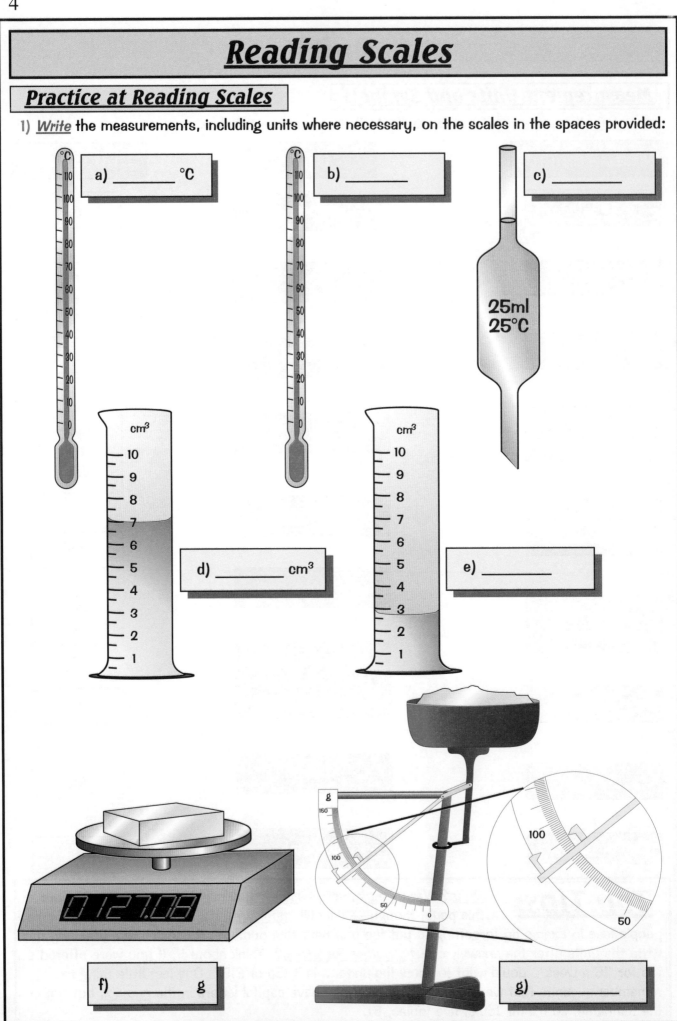

a) _____ °C

b) _____

c) _____

25ml
25°C

d) _____ cm³

e) _____

f) _____ g

g) _____

Reading Scales

Mostly Rulers...

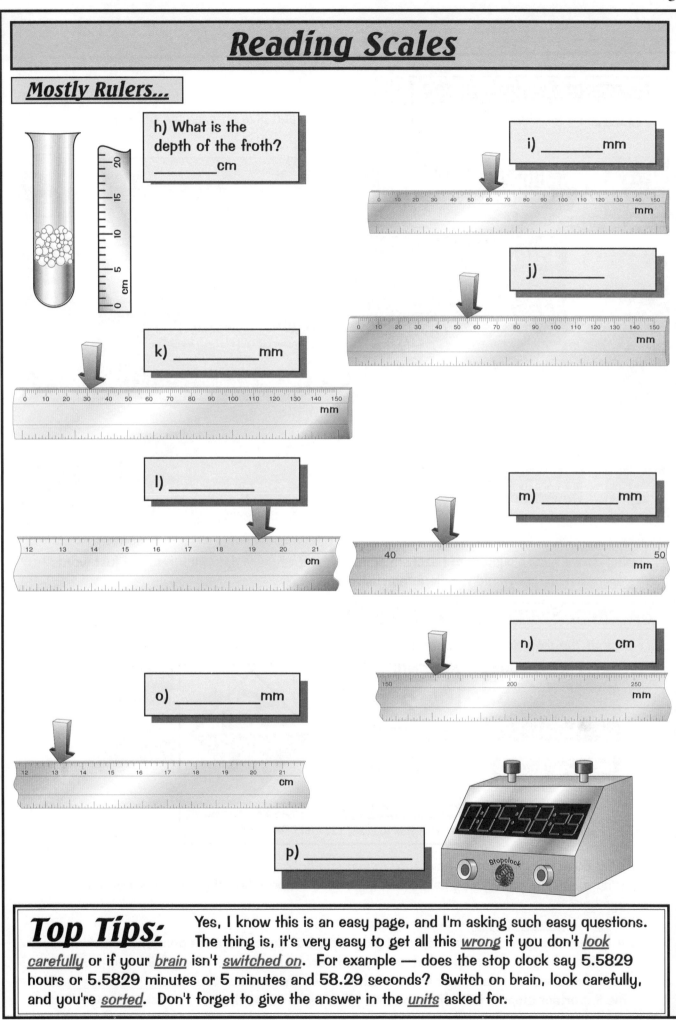

h) What is the
depth of the froth?
_____cm

i) _____mm

j) _____

k) _____mm

l) _____

m) _____mm

n) _____cm

o) _____mm

p) _____

Top Tips: Yes, I know this is an easy page, and I'm asking such easy questions. The thing is, it's very easy to get all this _wrong_ if you don't _look carefully_ or if your _brain_ isn't _switched on_. For example — does the stop clock say 5.5829 hours or 5.5829 minutes or 5 minutes and 58.29 seconds? Switch on brain, look carefully, and you're _sorted_. Don't forget to give the answer in the _units_ asked for.

Hazards

Hazchem Symbols in the Lab

1) *Link up* the hazchem symbols with their description, and give an example of each:

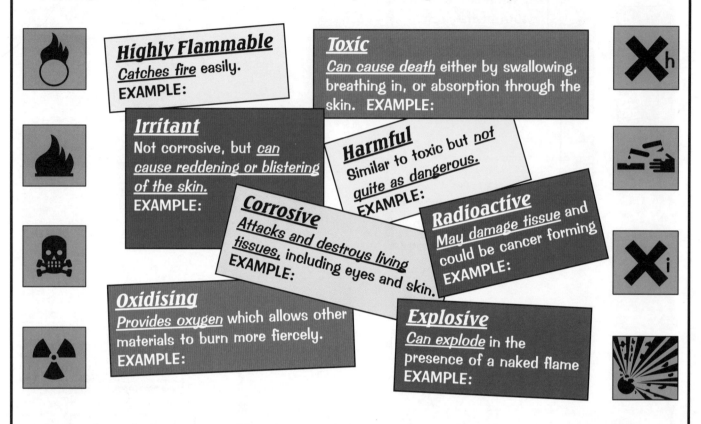

Highly Flammable
Catches fire easily.
EXAMPLE:

Toxic
Can cause death either by swallowing, breathing in, or absorption through the skin. EXAMPLE:

Irritant
Not corrosive, but *can cause reddening or blistering of the skin.*
EXAMPLE:

Harmful
Similar to toxic but *not* quite as dangerous.
EXAMPLE:

Corrosive
Attacks and destroys living tissues, including eyes and skin.
EXAMPLE:

Radioactive
May damage tissue and could be cancer forming
EXAMPLE:

Oxidising
Provides oxygen which allows other materials to burn more fiercely.
EXAMPLE:

Explosive
Can explode in the presence of a naked flame
EXAMPLE:

2) Why do we have a system of hazchem symbols, and why are they pictures, not just words?

3) *Describe* how you would handle a "corrosive chemical".

Hazchem Symbols Outside the Lab

4) *Look at the following information from the side of a chemical tanker.*

Information for the emergency services so they can take the correct action

HAZCHEM
2 PE

UN NO.
2031
Nitric Acid

Hazchem symbol

CORROSIVE

Manufacturer

UN reference number

Tells police who to contact

SPECIALIST ADVICE
Workington (01234) 123456

THE ACE CHEMICAL COMPANY

a) Why does the information have a *hazchem symbol*?

b) Why might the emergency services require *more* information than just the hazchem symbol?

c) Why is a *phone number* always included?

d) A tanker overturns in a crowded shopping area, but doesn't crack open. The Hazchem label tells the emergency services that its contents are corrosive, requiring full body protection when handled, but that they can be washed down the drains. Write a *short summary* of the important steps a fire officer handling this tanker should take.

Hazards

Hazards in the Laboratory

5) *List* ten *safety hazards* you can see in this laboratory.

Hazards:

1) _____
2) _____
3) _____
4) _____
5) _____

6) _____
7) _____
8) _____
9) _____
10) _____

6) What could *result* from eating food or drink in a laboratory?

7) What is the *correct way* of lighting a Bunsen burner?

8) Why is it *advisable* to use a heat-proof mat when heating a beaker of liquid on a gauze and tripod?

9) *Make a list* of ten lab rules or guidelines that you would give to a younger student, to ensure that they acted sensibly in a laboratory.

Top Tips:

I'm sure you already know that safety in the lab is important. And there's not really much to it. Basically, you've gotta use a little common sense. *Think* first, follow instructions, *don't* touch stuff you know you shouldn't, and think about *other people's safety* as well as your own. Even if you think you know it all already, it's well worth going through these questions just to *make sure* you do know how to *really* be safe in your practical lessons.

Prefixes

Symbols and Prefixes used for Multipliers

Prefixes are added before any unit to show how BIG or how SMALL the number is.

Example:

1 kilogram = 1000g   "kilo-" means 1000 times or 10^3 times the number.

So 1kg = 1000g   and   1kN = 1000N

Common Prefixes

	Prefix	symbol
10^9	giga	G
10^6	mega	M
10^3	kilo	k
10^2	hecto	h
10	deca	da

	Prefix	symbol
10^{-1}	deci	d
10^{-2}	centi	c
10^{-3}	milli	m
10^{-6}	micro	μ
10^{-9}	nano	n

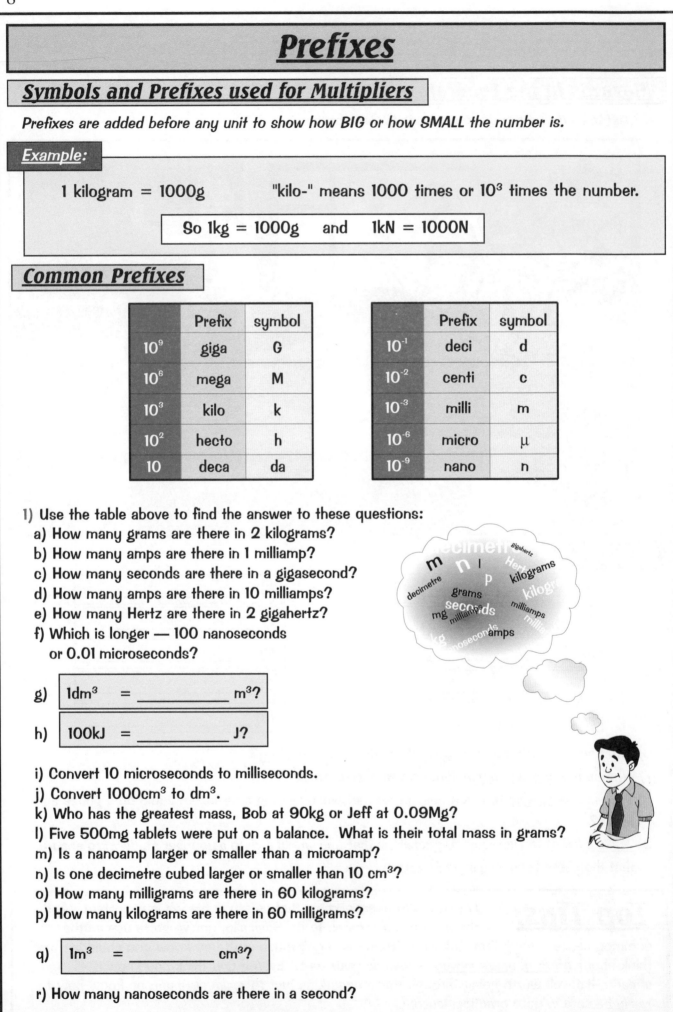

1) Use the table above to find the answer to these questions:
   a) How many grams are there in 2 kilograms?
   b) How many amps are there in 1 milliamp?
   c) How many seconds are there in a gigasecond?
   d) How many amps are there in 10 milliamps?
   e) How many Hertz are there in 2 gigahertz?
   f) Which is longer — 100 nanoseconds
      or 0.01 microseconds?

   g) | $1dm^3$ = _____ m^3? |

   h) | 100kJ = _____ J? |

   i) Convert 10 microseconds to milliseconds.
   j) Convert $1000cm^3$ to dm^3.
   k) Who has the greatest mass, Bob at 90kg or Jeff at 0.09Mg?
   l) Five 500mg tablets were put on a balance. What is their total mass in grams?
   m) Is a nanoamp larger or smaller than a microamp?
   n) Is one decimetre cubed larger or smaller than 10 cm^3?
   o) How many milligrams are there in 60 kilograms?
   p) How many kilograms are there in 60 milligrams?

   q) | $1m^3$ = _____ cm^3? |

   r) How many nanoseconds are there in a second?

Prefixes

More Questions on Prefixes...

1) Which of the following are _correct_ and which are _wrong_?

a) kg   e) μa   i) gHZ   m) DM3   q) Kc
b) KN   f) μV   j) mC   n) nv   r) mA
c) kn   g) Gm   k) Dm   o) dm³   s) Ghz
d) MA   h) KA   l) Kn   p) ma   t) kG

2) _Complete_ the following:

a) 1000g = _____ kg
b) 100g = _____ kg
c) 100kg = _____ g
d) 0.1kJ = _____ J
e) 1dm³ = _____ cm³
f) 1dm³ = _____ m³
g) 1dm³ = _____ ml
h) 0.01GA = _____ MA
i) 0.01GA = _____ A
j) 15mA = _____ A
k) 20mA = _____ μA
l) 5m = _____ km
m) 1500ns = _____ s
n) 100cm³ = _____ l
o) 100cm = _____ mm

3) To get an idea of the scale of things in this world, _match up_ the following quantities with the correct numbers and then _write in_ the _correct unit_ (from the list below) for each quantity.
Units: s, m, V, W, m/s, kg, No Units.

Quantity	Number	Units
a) How many seconds are there in a year?	230	
b) How big is an atom of hydrogen?	3	
c) What is mains voltage?	2,400	
d) How many volts would a torch run off?	31,536,000	
e) How many volts would a personal stereo run off?	6.02×10^{23}	
f) What is the wattage of a kitchen kettle?	approx. 110	
g) How many atoms are there in a mole of carbon?	10^{-10}	
h) How many atoms are there in half a mole of carbon?	3	
i) How many elements are there?	4.6×10^{16}	
j) Radius of a proton	6.37×10^{6}	
k) Radius of the Earth	3.00×10^{8}	
l) Distance to the nearest star other than the Sun	3.01×10^{23}	
m) Speed of light	27	
n) Speed of sound in air	10^{-15}	
o) Fastest sprinter in the world	9.11×10^{-31}	
p) Motorway speed limit	55	
q) Fastest land animal in the world	12	
r) Mass of an electron	31	
s) Mass of an average woman	330	

Top Tips:
You've got to get your units right in the Exam, it's _mega-important_ — and that includes using the _correct prefix_. So many marks get lost because the answer isn't complete without the unit — so get your units sorted out. You've really got to know your nanos from your micros — or the answer you put down will be _wrong_.

An Apparatus Crossword

A Crossword...

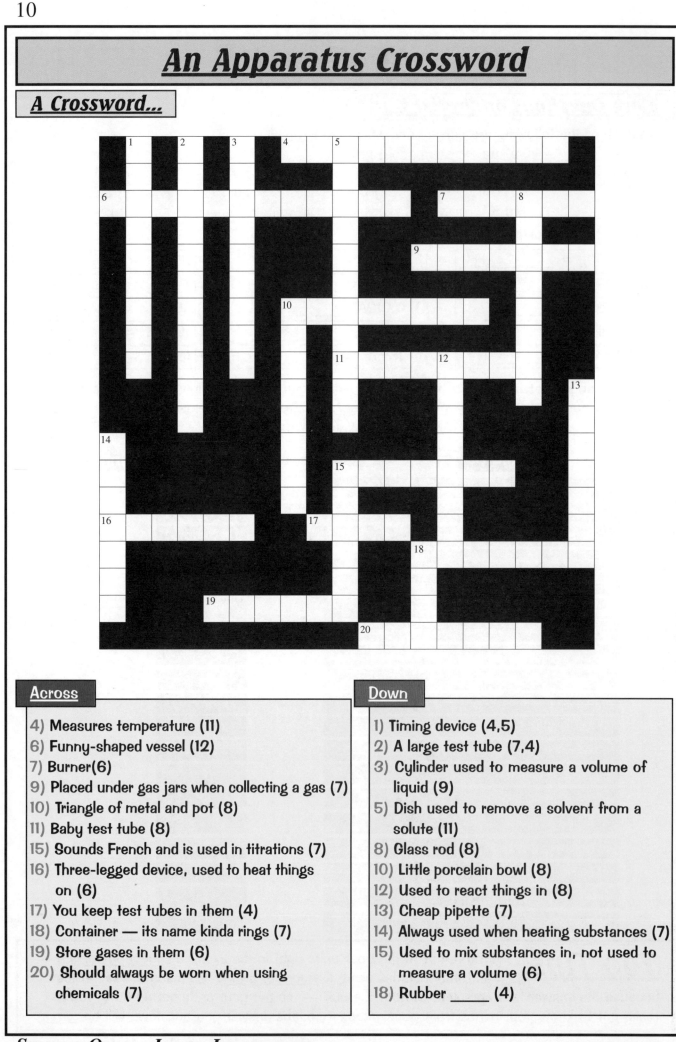

Across

4) Measures temperature (11)
6) Funny-shaped vessel (12)
7) Burner(6)
9) Placed under gas jars when collecting a gas (7)
10) Triangle of metal and pot (8)
11) Baby test tube (8)
15) Sounds French and is used in titrations (7)
16) Three-legged device, used to heat things on (6)
17) You keep test tubes in them (4)
18) Container — its name kinda rings (7)
19) Store gases in them (6)
20) Should always be worn when using chemicals (7)

Down

1) Timing device (4,5)
2) A large test tube (7,4)
3) Cylinder used to measure a volume of liquid (9)
5) Dish used to remove a solvent from a solute (11)
8) Glass rod (8)
10) Little porcelain bowl (8)
12) Used to react things in (8)
13) Cheap pipette (7)
14) Always used when heating substances (7)
15) Used to mix substances in, not used to measure a volume (6)
18) Rubber _____ (4)

Charts and Graphs

Which Graph to use for your Results

1) *You can use any of these graph types for the results that you might get in an investigation.*

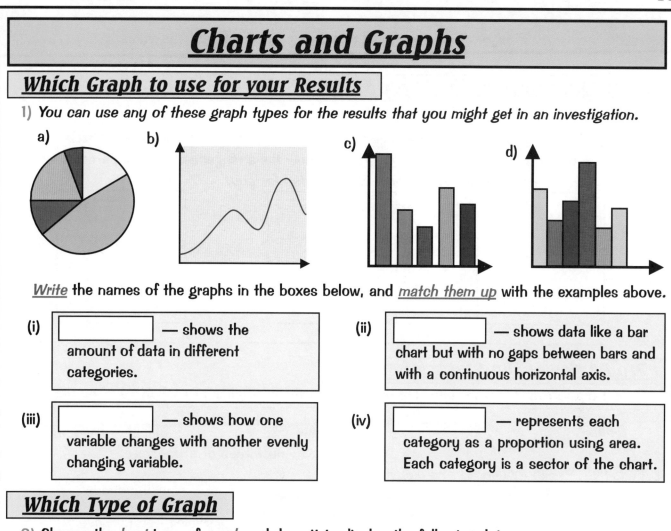

a)   b)   c)   d)

Write the names of the graphs in the boxes below, and *match them up* with the examples above.

(i) [   ] — shows the amount of data in different categories.

(ii) [   ] — shows data like a bar chart but with no gaps between bars and with a continuous horizontal axis.

(iii) [   ] — shows how one variable changes with another evenly changing variable.

(iv) [   ] — represents each category as a proportion using area. Each category is a sector of the chart.

Which Type of Graph

2) Choose the *best* type of *graph* and draw it to display the following data.

a)

Element	% element in the sea
oxygen	85.7
hydrogen	10.8
chlorine	1.9
sodium	1.1
magnesium	0.14
other	0.36

b)

Element	Cost (£/kg)
lithium	207
iron	1.5
carbon	5
chlorine	59
copper	10

c)

Time (s)	Vol. hydrogen (cm^3)
0	0.0
1	2.2
2	3.6
3	4.4
4	5.2
5	5.5
6	5.5

Choosing the Best Type of Graph

3) State *which graph* you would use for the following.

a) To show how long *different lengths* of magnesium ribbon take to react with acid.

b) To show the *% composition* of total elements in the human body.

c) To show for *how long* three different sized lumps of limestone will react with acid.

d) To show the *monthly sales*, for a year, of a GCSE Chemistry revision book.

Top Tips: Yes, it's basic stuff again, but you do need to know it. Remember, you've got to be able to record data so that *someone else* could look at it and *understand it perfectly*. Don't forget where *each* type of graph or chart is *best used*. You'll use graphs to display experimental data in your assessment work — remember, it counts for 25% of your overall grade. You'll get OK marks for drawing *best fit* lines, but more marks come from *interpreting* the patterns and bringing in some of your *plentiful scientific knowledge*.

SECTION ONE — IN THE LABORATORY

The Three States of Matter

Basic Questions on the Three States of Matter

1) Name the *three states* of matter.

2) Name the *theory* that explains the major differences between these states of matter.

3) In each of the boxes below, *draw a diagram* to show the arrangements of the particles in these three states of matter *(they have been started for you)*.

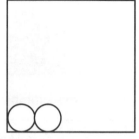

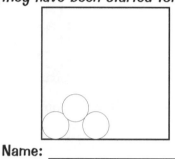

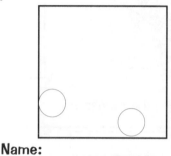

Name: _____   Name: _____   Name: _____

Properties of the States of Matter

4) Sort the following phrases into lists that describe the properties of each state of matter.

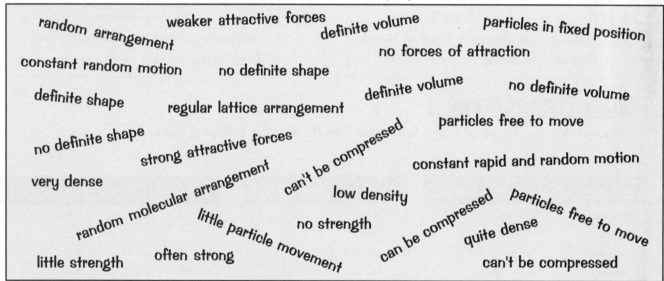

weaker attractive forces

random arrangement

definite volume

particles in fixed position

no forces of attraction

constant random motion   no definite shape

definite shape   regular lattice arrangement   definite volume   no definite volume

no definite shape   strong attractive forces   particles free to move

very dense   random molecular arrangement   can't be compressed   constant rapid and random motion

low density

little particle movement   no strength   can be compressed   particles free to move   quite dense

little strength   often strong   can't be compressed

a) Which state of matter is the *strongest*? Why?

b) Which state will have the least particles in a given volume? *Explain* why.

c) For a given substance, which state of it will have the most energy? *Explain* why.

d) Which *state* will water be in at: -10°C, 10°C, 110°C (under normal atmospheric pressure)? What is the *common name* for each state?

e) Why is it *difficult* to squash liquids? *Give an example* of something that might use this property.

f) *Gases can be squashed.* What does this tell you about the distance between gas particles?

g) *Explain* how a gas exerts pressure on the sides of its container.

h) What would happen to the *pressure* of a gas if you increased its temperature in a rigid container? *Why* would this happen?

Top Tips:
There's a lot of little *details* here that you need to get to grips with — it's really important that you know *all* the differences between solids, liquids and gases. You've also got to know *how* their properties make them suitable for various jobs. The thing to remember is that it's *how close* the particles are and *how fast* they're moving about that explains their *physical properties* — have another look through the lists in question 4.

The Three States of Matter

Changing the State of Matter

1) Give four _everyday examples_ of each of the three states of matter.

2) _Complete_ the following diagram by naming each change of state — A, B, C, and D.

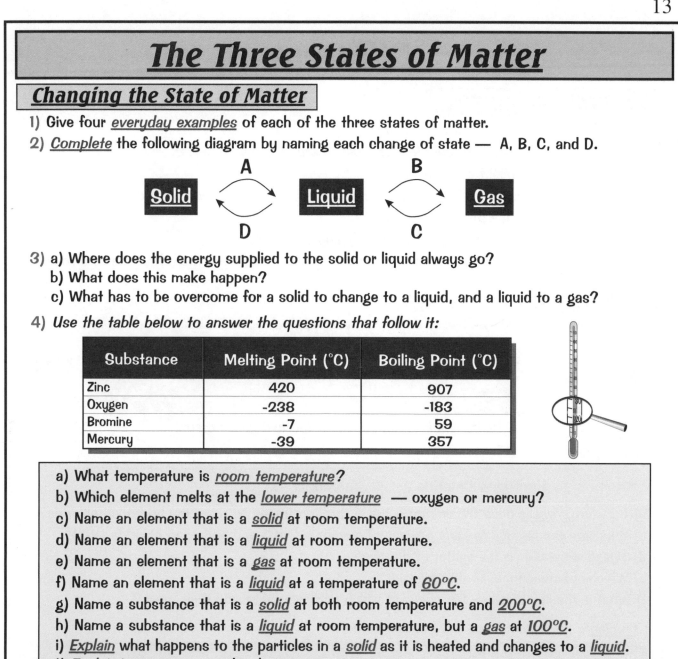

3) a) Where does the energy supplied to the solid or liquid always go?
   b) What does this make happen?
   c) What has to be overcome for a solid to change to a liquid, and a liquid to a gas?

4) _Use the table below to answer the questions that follow it:_

Substance	Melting Point (°C)	Boiling Point (°C)
Zinc	420	907
Oxygen	-238	-183
Bromine	-7	59
Mercury	-39	357

a) What temperature is _room temperature_?
b) Which element melts at the _lower temperature_ — oxygen or mercury?
c) Name an element that is a _solid_ at room temperature.
d) Name an element that is a _liquid_ at room temperature.
e) Name an element that is a _gas_ at room temperature.
f) Name an element that is a _liquid_ at a temperature of _60°C_.
g) Name a substance that is a _solid_ at both room temperature and _200°C_.
h) Name a substance that is a _liquid_ at room temperature, but a _gas_ at _100°C_.
i) _Explain_ what happens to the particles in a _solid_ as it is heated and changes to a _liquid_.
j) _Explain_ in your own words what _evaporation_ is.

Cooling Curves

5) _Look at the graph opposite. This shows how the temperature of wax changes as it is cooled. Explain_ why the graph has two flat sections.

   (_Words to use:_ Condensing, freezing, temperature, particles, flat sections).

6) _Describe_ what happens to the particles in water when it freezes.

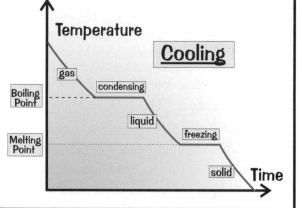

Top Tips:
Melting, boiling, freezing, evaporating — all the fun stuff that substances can do... The _big point_ that you've really got to know is that _changes_ of _state_ mean that _heat energy_ is going _in_ or _out_ of the substance. Basically, if you give energy to a substance, the particles can move faster. You've got to be able to say what's _actually happening_ in the four changes of state in question 2b. One last _important_ thing — don't forget why you get _flat bits_ on heating and cooling graphs.

Diffusion

Questions on Diffusion

1) _Define_ the term _diffusion_ and use the word "_diffuse_" in a suitable sentence.
2) _Some purple potassium manganate(VII) crystals are dissolved in water._
   Describe what you might see happening.
3) _Bromine will diffuse through a vacuum very quickly._ _Why_ is this and what does it tell you about the _speed_ of the bromine molecules?
4) _Bromine diffuses slowly through air._ _Explain why_ it is slow.
5) Why is it possible to _smell_ someone's aftershave or perfume from the other side of a room?

The Nitty Gritty of Diffusion

6) _The diagram below shows pieces of cotton wool soaked in ammonia and hydrochloric acid._

HCl  Ring of white ammonium chloride powder **NH$_3$**

White smoke appears where the two gases meet.

a) _Complete_ the equation:

Hydrogen Chloride $_{(g)}$ + Ammonia → _____

b) By what _process_ does the ammonia travel through the air to meet the hydrogen chloride?
c) What are the _relative formula masses_ of ammonia (NH$_3$) and hydrogen chloride (HCl)?
d) _Which_ substance is the lighter of the two?   _(H=1, N=14, Cl=35.5)._
e) Which substance moves the _quickest_?
f) What is the link between the _speed_ at which particles move and their _mass_?

7) _Complete_ these sentences using these words:

fast	big	small	slow	kinetic

At a certain temperature the particles in a gas have a particular amount of movement energy (_____ energy). If the particles are _____, then the speed at which they move will be high and so diffusion will be _____. If the particles are _____, then the speed of the particles is small and so diffusion will be _____.

8) _If the temperature of a gas is increased then the average kinetic energy of the particles also increases._ _What effect_ might this have on the rate of diffusion?
9) Which will diffuse _faster_: a gas at room temperature or a gas at body temperature?
10) Which will diffuse _slower_: a gas at body temperature or a gas at the boiling point of water?
11) Why do solid air fresheners smell _stronger_ on a warm day?
12) _Draw a picture_ to show how the particles in an air freshener can move from where there are a lot of them to where there are only a few of them.

Top Tips: Diffusion just means that substances _spread out_ and _merge together_. Simple. Remember that it happens because the particles in liquids and gases are all moving about _randomly_, and so eventually they spread all over the place and the concentrations get evened out. Get used to using words like "_kinetic energy_" and "_molecular mass_", because they're _key words_ that show examiners you know what you're on about.

Atoms and Molecules

From the diagrams, choose the letter of the pictures that best describe:

1) A *pure* element.
2) A *pure* compound.
3) A *mixture* of elements.
4) A *mixture* of compounds.
5) An example of molecules made from just *two elements*.
6) An example of molecules made from *three elements*.
7) Which example could be *water*?
8) Which example could be *carbon monoxide*?

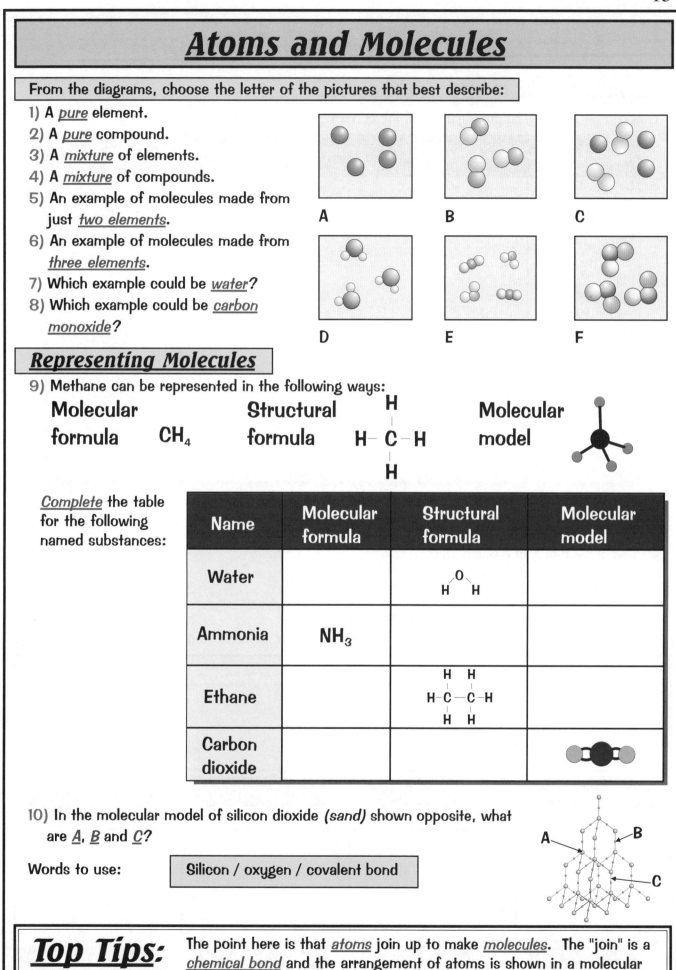

A   B   C

D   E   F

Representing Molecules

9) Methane can be represented in the following ways:

Molecular formula CH_4

Structural formula
$$H - \underset{\underset{\displaystyle H}{|}}{\overset{\overset{\displaystyle H}{|}}{C}} - H$$

Molecular model

Complete the table for the following named substances:

Name	Molecular formula	Structural formula	Molecular model
Water		O with H and H	
Ammonia	NH_3		
Ethane		H H H–C–C–H H H	
Carbon dioxide			

10) In the molecular model of silicon dioxide *(sand)* shown opposite, what are *A*, *B* and *C*?

Words to use: Silicon / oxygen / covalent bond

A ← → B

← C

Top Tips:
The point here is that *atoms* join up to make *molecules*. The "join" is a *chemical bond* and the arrangement of atoms is shown in a molecular model. You can show a molecule on paper as a *molecular formula* or a *structural formula* or you can build a *three dimensional model* with little balls and sticks, which is more fun.

Elements Mixtures and Compounds

Examples of Elements, Mixtures and Compounds

1) _Complete the table_ by putting a tick in the correct column. The first one has been done for you.

Substance	Element	Mixture	Compound
Copper	✓		
Air			
Distilled water			
Brine			
Sodium			
Cupro-nickel			
Sodium chloride			
Copper sulphate			
Sulphur			
Oxygen			
Sea water			
Bronze			
Petrol			
Blue ink			
Steel			
Steam			
Milk			

Definitions

2) Give a definition of an element.

3) Give a definition of a compound.

4) Give a definition of a mixture.

5) What is an alloy?

6) Why is an alloy not classed as a compound?

7) In the boxes below _draw out circles_ to represent atoms of elements and molecules of compounds.

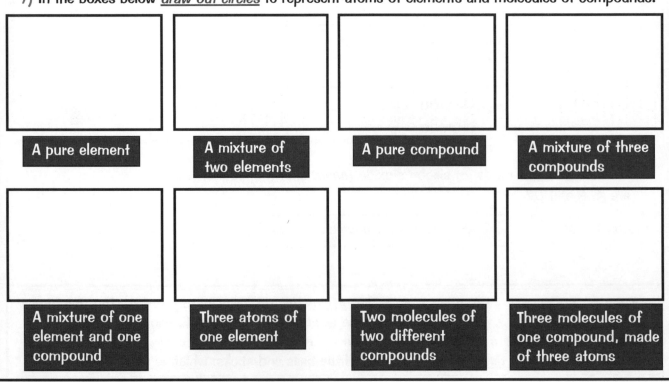

| A pure element | A mixture of two elements | A pure compound | A mixture of three compounds |

| A mixture of one element and one compound | Three atoms of one element | Two molecules of two different compounds | Three molecules of one compound, made of three atoms |

Solubility

Problems and Solutions

1) A solution is made by adding a solute to a solvent. <u>Complete</u> the sentences:

"When putting coffee granules into a cup of boiling water, the granules are a _____ and the water is a _____. Therefore a cup of coffee is a _____".

2) Below is a table of different substances and their solubilities at different temperatures. The solubility is the amount of the substance that will dissolve in a given amount of water.

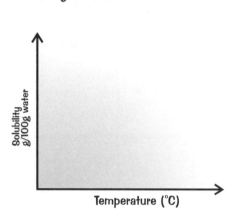

SUBSTANCE	SOLUBILITY (g/100g) water				
	10°C	30°C	50°C	70°C	90°C
Ammonium Chloride	33	41	50	60	71
Copper Sulphate	17	24	33	47	67
Lead Nitrate	44	60	78	97	117
Potassium Chlorate	5	10	18	30	46
Potassium Chloride	31	37	43	48	53
Potassium Nitrate	21	45	83	135	203
Sodium Nitrate	80	96	114	135	161

a) <u>Plot a graph</u> of solubility against temperature, with each substance in a different colour.

b) Which is the most <u>soluble</u> substance at i) 10°C   ii) 30°C   iii) 50°C   iv) 70°C   v) 90°C?

c) What is the <u>solubility</u> of potassium nitrate (in g/100g water) at i) 15°C   ii) 60°C   iii) 75°C?
   (Hint: look at your graph for this question)

d) Which substance's solubility <u>changes the most</u> over this temperature range? How do you know?

e) If you cooled saturated potassium nitrate solution from 60°C to 15°C, <u>how much</u> salt (in grams) would come out of solution per 100g? <u>Show your working out</u>.

f) If you cooled saturated potassium chlorate solution from 60°C to 15°C, <u>how much</u> salt would come out of solution?

Solubility Calculations

3) 4g of a solid is found to make a saturated solution with 50g of water.
   What is its <u>solubility</u> in g/100g of water?

4) 4g of a solid is found to make a saturated solution with 25g of water.
   What is its <u>solubility</u> in g/100g of water?

5) 4g of a solid is found to make a saturated solution with 20g of water.
   What is its <u>solubility</u> in g/100g of water?

6) <u>Describe</u> how you could measure the approximate solubility of sugar in water at 50°C in the lab. (What apparatus will you need, what you will measure and how will you measure it?)

7) On a hot day an open bottle of fizzy drink will go flat quicker outside than in a refrigerator. What does this tell you about the link between the solubility of gases and temperature? Complete this sentence:

"The hotter the liquid, the _____ soluble are gases in that liquids."

Top Tips: This page really is about as hard as it could get with solubility questions. If they give you <u>data</u> and ask you to <u>draw a graph</u>, you usually get all the answers from the graph. Make sure you know these: <u>solvent</u>, <u>solution</u>, <u>solute</u> and <u>solubility</u>.

Types of Materials

Examples of the Different Types of Materials

1) _Complete_ the table below using the following words: _high, medium, low, good, poor._

Type of material	Common Examples	Tensile strength (how difficult it is to break apart)	Compressive strength (how difficult it is to crush)	Flexibility (how easy it is to bend)	Electrical conductivity (how easily it lets electricity through)	Thermal conductivity (how easily it lets heat through)	Porosity (how well it soaks up water)	Cost of manufacture
Metals								Expensive
Ceramics								Cheap
Glass								Expensive
Plastics								Fairly expensive
Fibres								Natural: cheap, synthetics: fairly expensive

Word Puzzle

2) Find the following types of materials or substances by _rearranging_ the letters:

a) SIDAC		g) BRISEF	
b) LISKALA		h) SCLASTIP	
c) LOLYAS		i) DOOW	
d) SREFTILISER		j) MARCCISE	
e) SPOAS		k) LAGESSS	
f) SLATS		l) TALEMS	

Top Tips:
Basically, the properties of a substance are to do with _how_ the atoms or molecules are _joined up_, which is why we need to know about atoms and how they bond. High _tensile strength_ and high _melting point_ in a substance both mean it has _strong bonds_. Look at the materials in Question 1 — think about how strongly bonded together the molecules are, and if there are _free electrons_ or _ions_ to conduct _electricity_. There's plenty of stuff about how the atoms bond together coming up, so be patient, sit tight, et cetera.

Atoms

Properties of Atoms

1) *Answer these questions on atoms:*
   a) What is an *atom*?
   b) *How many* different subatomic particles make up an atom?
   c) What are their *names*?
   d) What is a *nucleus*?
   e) What is an *electron shell*?

2) *Complete the labels* A, B and C on the diagram opposite.

3) *Complete* the table below:

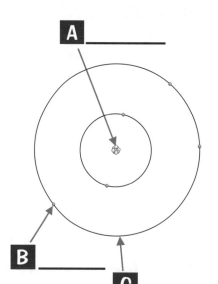

Particle	Mass	Charge	Where it is found
Proton	1		
Electron		-1	
Neutron			In the nucleus

4) *More details on atoms:*
   a) *Where* is most of the mass in an atom concentrated?
   b) What is in between the *nucleus* and the *electrons*?

5) *An atom is about 10^{-10}m in diameter. How many* would fit in a line across a pin head 0.1mm wide?

6) *Nuclear reactions affect the nucleus. What do* *chemical reactions* affect?

7) *All atoms are neutral.* If an atom has seven electrons then *how many* protons does it have?

8) *Answer these questions on the atomic number and mass number of an element:*
   a) What does the *atomic number* tell us?
   b) What does the *mass number* tell us?
   c) What do the letters *A* and *Z* in the diagram stand for? What is *A - Z*?
   d) *How many* protons are there in an atom of lithium?
   e) *How many* electrons are there in an atom of lithium?
   f) *How many* neutrons are there in an atom of lithium?
   g) Which *number* (mass or atomic) determines what element an atom is?

$A \searrow^7$

Li

$Z \searrow^3$

9) *Calculate* the number of protons, electrons and neutrons in the following:
   a) Carbon ($^{12}_{6}\text{C}$)   b) Potassium ($^{39}_{19}\text{K}$)   c) Hydrogen ($^{1}_{1}\text{H}$).

Isotopes

10) *Some questions on isotopes:*
    a) What are *isotopes*?
    b) *Give an example* of an isotope used in dating old objects.
    c) *Uranium 235 and Uranium 238 are isotopes.* Are they chemically different? *Explain* why.

11) *Calculate* the number of protons, electrons and neutrons in:

    a) Deuterium ($^{2}_{1}\text{H}$)   b) Tritium ($^{3}_{1}\text{H}$)

12) *76% of chlorine is ^{35}Cl, and 24% is ^{37}Cl.* What is its *relative atomic mass*?

Top Tips:
There's a fair bit of new terminology on this page — but that's science for you. It's *really important* that you know the difference between *atomic* number and *mass* number — and that you know what it all *means*. Doing questions like this is excellent practice — come the Exam, you'll be well equipped to win yourself lots of lovely marks. Bet you can't wait...

Electron Arrangement

Electrons

1) An atom can be compared to the solar system. _Explain_ the similarity.
2) What keeps the electrons _attracted_ to the nucleus?
3) Give _another_ name for an electron orbit.
4) _Complete_ the table to show the sizes of the electron shells:

Electron shell	Maximum number of electrons in the shell
1st	
2nd	
3rd	

Electronic Configuration

5) _Complete_ the table below showing the properties of the first 20 elements (_you will need the Periodic Table at the front of the book_).

Element	Symbol	Atomic Number	Mass Number	Number of Protons	Number of Electrons	Number of Neutrons	Electronic Configuration	Group Number
Hydrogen	H	1	1	1	1	0	1	—
Helium	He	2	4	2	2	2	2	0
Lithium	Li						2, 1	1
Beryllium								2
Boron				5				
Carbon								
Nitrogen		7						
Oxygen					8			
Fluorine							2, 7	
Neon								
Sodium		11						1
Magnesium								
Aluminium		13	27	13	13	14	2, 8, 3	3
Silicon								
Phosphorus								
Sulphur	S							
Chlorine								
Argon								
Potassium								
Calcium						20		2

6) Look at the table. What is the link between _group number_ and _number of outer electrons_?

7) What is the link between the _Noble gases_ (group 0) and _full outer shells_?

8) _Iodine is in group 7_ — _how many_ electrons does it have in its outer electron shell?

9) _Silicon is in group 4_ — _how many_ electrons does it have in its outer electron shell?

10) _Xenon is in group 0_ — _how many_ electrons does it have in its outer electron shell?

11) The _number of electrons_ in the outer shell governs which _property_ of the element?

12) An atom of element **X** has two outer electrons that do not fill the outer shell.

   a) _Name_ its group.

   b) Is it a _metal_ or _non-metal_?

   c) Name _another_ element with similar chemical properties to **X**.

Covalent Bonding

Dot and Cross Diagrams

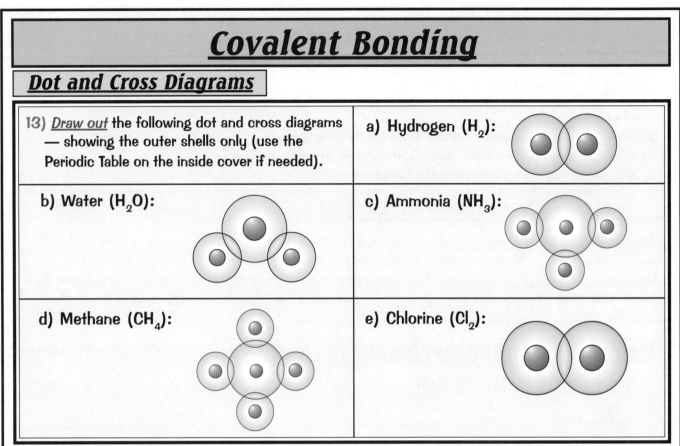

13) <u>Draw out</u> the following dot and cross diagrams — showing the outer shells only (use the Periodic Table on the inside cover if needed).

a) Hydrogen (H_2):

b) Water (H_2O):

c) Ammonia (NH_3):

d) Methane (CH_4):

e) Chlorine (Cl_2):

14) *A single covalent bond involves sharing a pair of electrons. What does a <u>double covalent bond</u> involve?*

15) What is the <u>full electronic configuration</u> of oxygen?

16) How many <u>more</u> electrons does oxygen need in order to fill its outer shell?

17) <u>Which element</u> has the electron configuration 2,8?

18) *Oxygen can attain a full shell by forming a double bond with itself. <u>Using crosses</u> fill in the double bond to the right and label it. Then fill in the other electrons.*

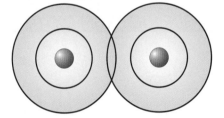

19) *Carbon dioxide has the formula CO_2 — drawn out in the diagram below. <u>Fill in</u> the electrons in the <u>outer shells</u> of the oxygen and carbon atoms.*

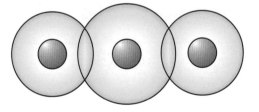

20) <u>Fill in</u> the electron configuration for the molecule of ethene (C_2H_4) shown here:

Top Tips: The ability to draw out dot and cross diagrams shows an examiner that you <u>really</u> know your Chemistry. You'll need to know <u>all</u> the examples you've done on this page for a high grade — especially the molecules with double bonds. The bottom line here is that atoms like to have a <u>full outer shell</u> of electrons, so some atoms will <u>share electrons</u> so that they "<u>feel</u>" like they've got a full outer shell.

24

Ions

Questions on Ions

1) What is an *ion*?
2) Give *two* examples of ions made from single atoms.
3) Give *two* examples of ions made from several atoms.
4) *Complete* this paragraph using the words provided:

| -ve | protons | negatively charged | neutral | positively charged |

Atoms are electrically _____ because they have equal numbers of _____ (+ve) and electrons (____). If electrons are taken away from a metal atom or hydrogen, then it becomes _____ _____ because it has less electrons than protons. If electrons are added to a non-metal atom, it becomes _____ _____ because it then has more electrons than protons.

Example 1: Positive Ions (metals and hydrogen)

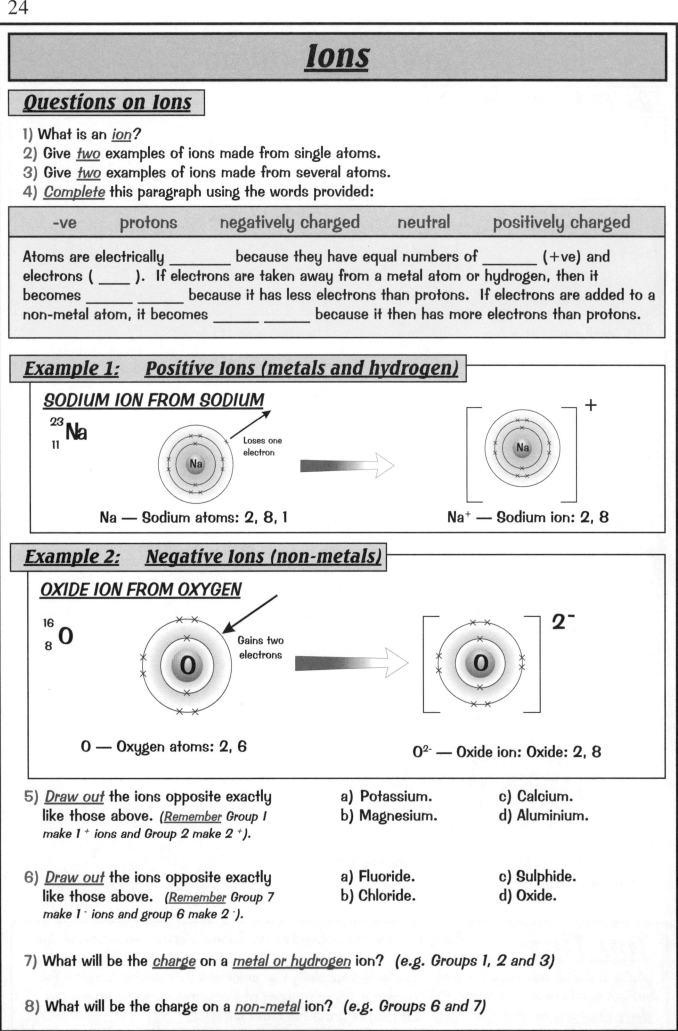

SODIUM ION FROM SODIUM

$^{23}_{11}Na$

Loses one electron

Na — Sodium atoms: 2, 8, 1

+

Na^+ — Sodium ion: 2, 8

Example 2: Negative Ions (non-metals)

OXIDE ION FROM OXYGEN

$^{16}_{8}O$

Gains two electrons

O — Oxygen atoms: 2, 6

2⁻

O^{2-} — Oxide ion: Oxide: 2, 8

5) *Draw out* the ions opposite exactly like those above. *(Remember* Group I make 1 ⁺ ions and Group 2 make 2 ⁺).
  a) Potassium.   c) Calcium.
  b) Magnesium.   d) Aluminium.

6) *Draw out* the ions opposite exactly like those above. *(Remember* Group 7 make 1 ⁻ ions and group 6 make 2 ⁻).
  a) Fluoride.   c) Sulphide.
  b) Chloride.   d) Oxide.

7) What will be the *charge* on a *metal or hydrogen* ion? *(e.g. Groups 1, 2 and 3)*

8) What will be the charge on a *non-metal* ion? *(e.g. Groups 6 and 7)*

SECTION TWO — CLASSIFYING MATERIALS

Ions

The Basics of Ionic Bonding

1) What is an ionic bond?

2) If an atom gains an electron, what charge does it have?

3) If an atom loses an electron, what charge does it have?

4) Why do sodium ions have a 1^+ charge?

5) Why do chloride ions have a 1^- charge?

6) What charge would you find on a Group 2 ion?

7) What charge would you find on a Group 6 ion?

8) Why is it rare to find a 4^+ ion of carbon?

9) What is a cation and what is an anion?

10) _Draw_ an electron configuration diagram to show what happens when a lithium atom reacts with a chlorine atom. Name the compound formed.

11) _Draw_ an electron configuration diagram to show what happens when a magnesium atom reacts with two chlorine atoms.

12) Why is sodium chloride neutral?

13) _Draw_ a picture to show the positions of sodium and chloride ions in a sodium chloride crystal.

14) Give the _formulae_ of magnesium oxide, sodium fluoride, sodium oxide, magnesium sulphate and sodium sulphate, using the following:

Mg^{2+} $\qquad$ Na^+ $\qquad$ SO_4^{2-} $\qquad$ F^- $\qquad$ O^{2-}

Some Examples of Ions

15) _Name_ the following ions:

a) Na^+ b) Cl^- c) S^{2-} d) NO_3^- e) SO_4^{2-} f) I^- g) F^- h) K^+ i) Ca^{2+} j) Mg^{2+} k) PO_4^{3-} l) H^+ m) Ba^{2+}

16) From the box below, choose:

SO_4^{2-}	Mg^{2+}	Kr	MgO	CO_2

a) an example of a gas consisting of _single atoms_.

b) an example of a substance made from _ions_.

c) an example of a substance made from _molecules_.

d) an example of a compound.

e) an example of an _ion_.

f) an example of a _molecular ion_ (compound ion).

Properties of Ionic Substances

17) Which in the following list are _general_ properties of an ionically bonded compound?

a) High boiling point	d) Non-conductor when melted
b) Usually dissolve in water	e) Weak forces hold molecules together
c) Conductor when solid	f) Non-crystalline

18) If any of the properties listed in question 17 are not properties of ionically bonded compounds then correct them (_e.g. if they've not got a high boiling point they must have a low one_).

Top Tips: _Ionic_ compounds are formed when electrons are _swapped_ between one atom and another, once again to get that sought-after _full-outer-shell_ feeling. Remember that they contain a _metal_ and a _non-metal_ — and don't forget which ions are _positive_ and which _negative_. You do also need to know all the _properties_ of ionic compounds.

Symbols, Formulae and Equations

Formulae and the Periodic Table

1) *Write out* the first twenty elements of the Periodic Table with their symbols.

2) *Write out* the symbols for the following:

| iron | lead | zinc | tin | copper |

3) *Complete* this table:

Name	Formula	Proportion of each element present in substance
Zinc oxide	ZnO	1 zinc 1 oxygen
Magnesium oxide		
	NaCl	
	HCl	
Sulphur dioxide		
		1 carbon 2 oxygen
		1 sodium 1 oxygen 1 hydrogen
Potassium hydroxide		
		1 calcium 1 carbon 3 oxygen
Copper sulphate		
Potassium Hydroxide		
	H_2SO_4	
		2 Iron 3 oxygen
	$MgCl_2$	
	H_2	
		2 Chlorine

4) *Complete* the following:

When **CHLORINE** reacts with a metal element to make an ionic compound it forms a **CHLOR**_____.

When **OXYGEN** reacts with a metal element to make an ionic compound it forms an **OX**_____.

When **SULPHUR** reacts with a metal element to make an ionic compound it forms a **SULPH**_____.

5) What name would you give to a compound made from *SODIUM* and *BROMINE*?

6) What name would you give to a compound made from *SODIUM* and *FLUORINE*?

7) If a compound has "—ate" at the end of its name, what *element* will be present?

8) *Some compounds have "—ite" at the end of their name, like sodium chlorite.*
   What *element* will be present if "—ite" is in the name of a compound?

9) Some toothpastes contain sodium monofluorophosphate. What *elements* do you think are present in this compound?

Simple Equations

10) *Complete* the following word equations:

a) Sodium	+	chlorine	→	_____ _____
b) Carbon	+	_____	→	Carbon dioxide
c) Sulphur	+	oxygen	→	_____ _____
d) Zinc	+	oxygen	→	_____ _____
e) _____	+	_____	→	Iron sulphide
f) Potassium	+	chlorine	→	_____ _____
g) Lead	+	oxygen	→	_____ _____
h) _____	+	_____	→	Calcium oxide

Symbols, Formulae and Equations

Formulae of Compounds

11)

1$^+$ ions	2+ ions	3+ ions	4+/4-	3-	2- ions	1- ions
Li$^+$ (lithium)	Mg^{2+} (magnesium)	Al^{3+} (aluminium)	Very rare	Fairly rare	O^{2-} (oxide)	F$^-$ (fluoride)
Na$^+$ (sodium)	Ca^{2+} (calcium)	Fe^{3+} (iron(III))			S^{2-} (sulphide)	Cl$^-$ (chloride)
K$^+$ (potassium)	Ba^{2+} (barium)	Cr^{3+} (chromium(III))				Br$^-$ (bromide)
Cu$^+$ (copper(I))	Cu^{2+} (copper(II))					I$^-$ (iodide)
Ag$^+$ (silver)	Fe^{2+} (iron(II))					NO$_3^-$ (nitrate)
H$^+$ (hydrogen)	Zn^{2+} (zinc)				SO$_4^{2-}$ (sulphate)	OH$^-$ (hydroxide)
NH$_4^+$ (ammonium)	Pb^{2+} (lead)				CO$_3^{2-}$ (carbonate)	HCO$_3^-$ (hydrogencarbonate)

Using the information above, fill in the correct ions and formulae in the table:

Compound	Positive ion	Negative ion	Formula
copper oxide	Cu^{2+}	O^{2-}	CuO
sodium chloride			
zinc sulphate			
aluminium iodide			
potassium hydroxide			
calcium carbonate			
zinc bromide			
potassium carbonate			
sodium sulphate			
potassium sulphate			
potassium nitrate			
lead sulphate			
magnesium bromide			
barium chloride			
silver nitrate			
sodium nitrate			

SECTION TWO — CLASSIFYING MATERIALS

Structures

Substances

1) Below is a diagram that classifies substances according to their structures.
   a) *Write in* the missing words in the *"structure"* boxes.
   b) The substances *in the box below* can be split into groups: write each in the correct *"example"* box in the diagram.

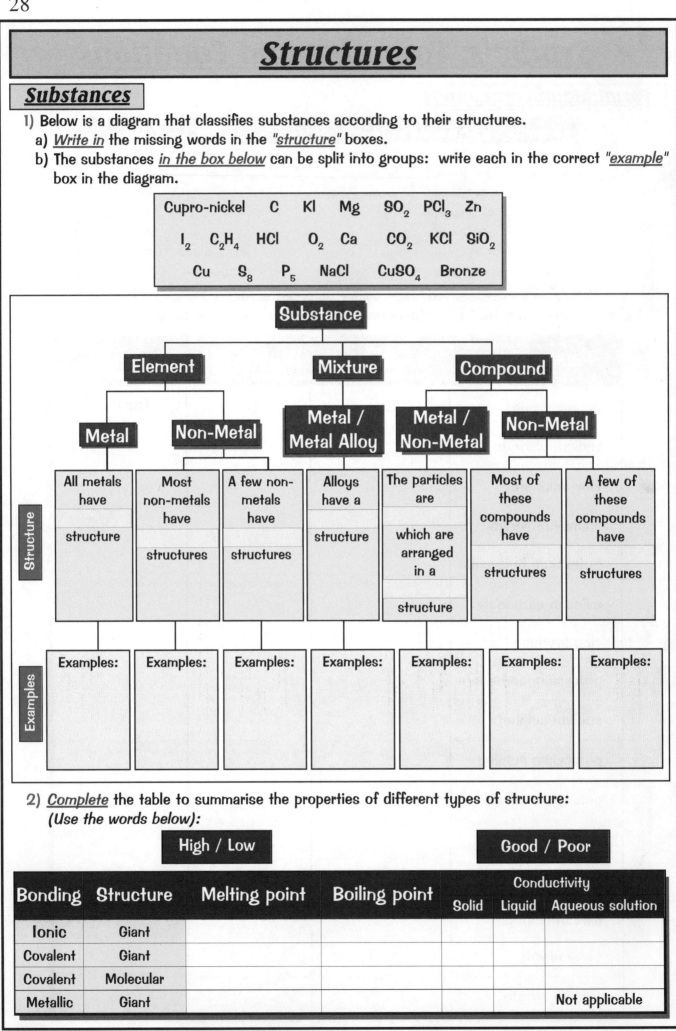

Cupro-nickel   C   KI   Mg SO_2 PCl_3 Zn

I_2 C_2H_4 HCl O_2 Ca CO_2 KCl SiO_2

Cu S_8 P_5 NaCl $CuSO_4$ Bronze

Substance

Element   Mixture   Compound

Metal   Non-Metal   Metal / Metal Alloy   Metal / Non-Metal   Non-Metal

Structure

All metals have _____ structure

Most non-metals have _____ structures

A few non-metals have _____ structures

Alloys have a _____ structure

The particles are _____ which are arranged in a _____ structure

Most of these compounds have _____ structures

A few of these compounds have _____ structures

Examples

Examples: Examples: Examples: Examples: Examples: Examples: Examples:

2) *Complete* the table to summarise the properties of different types of structure:
   (Use the words below):

High / Low   Good / Poor

Bonding	Structure	Melting point	Boiling point	Conductivity		
				Solid	Liquid	Aqueous solution
Ionic	Giant					
Covalent	Giant					
Covalent	Molecular					
Metallic	Giant					Not applicable

Structures

Physical and Chemical Properties

3) "Substances have physical properties because of their chemical properties". _Explain_ what this means and state whether or not you agree with it.

4) _Why_ are ionic substances generally brittle?

5) Why do most covalent substances _melt easily_?

6) _Which_ covalent substances do not melt easily?

7) Why do ionic substances only _conduct electricity_ when molten or when dissolved in water?

8) Referring to the diagram opposite, _explain_ why ionic crystals dissolve in water.

9) _Tick_ the correct column for each substance in the table below.

Substance	Non-Conductor	Conducts but doesn't alter	Conducts and alters
Graphite			
Molten sodium chloride			
Sodium chloride solution			
Mercury			
Sodium hydroxide (aq)			
Molten aluminium			
Molten lead iodide			
Copper			
Distilled water			
Kerosene (jet fuel)			
Aqueous solution of sugar			
Petrol			
Toluene			
Hydrogen chloride in solution			
Molten napthalene			
Molten sulphur			
A suspension of sulphur			
Urea			
Methanol			
Sulphuric acid			
Chloroethane			
Sea water			
Lead			
Magnesium			
Molten magnesium chloride			

Top Tips: If you've completed all these questions and got all of them right, then, yes, you know about the properties of different structures. If you haven't, then, surprise, surprise, you need to go back and try them again. Examiners are always wanting you to show that you know the properties of _giant_ and _molecular substances_, and can relate _properties_ to _structure_ — know your structures and get some easy marks...

Metals and Metallic Bonding

Metals and Structures

1) _Describe_ how an atom of iron joins up to other atoms in an iron bar.

2) Metals have "giant structures of atoms". What is a _giant structure_?

3) What are "_free electrons_", and where do they originate?

4) _Draw_ a diagram to show the metal ions and free electrons in a giant structure.

5) _Look at the table opposite:_

   a) _Complete_ the table.

   b) _Metals have the properties shown in the table because of their bonding._ What is the _name_ given to a bond in a metal?

Metal Property	Good Example	Reason	Exception (if any)
Strong			
Good Conductor of Heat			
Good Conductor of electricity			
Can be rolled into sheets (malleable)			
Can be drawn into wires (ductile)			

Alloys

6) What is an _alloy_?

7) Why do we _use_ metal alloys?

8) Look at the diagram below. _Explain_ why the alloy is _stronger_ than the pure metal.

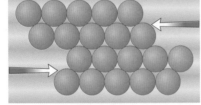

Pure Metal

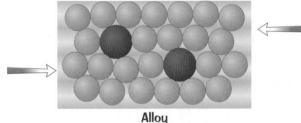

Alloy

The Right Metal for the Job

Metal	Melting Point (°C)	Boiling Point (°C)	Specific Heat Capacity (J/Kg/°C)	Density (g/cm³)	Electrical Conductivity (S/m)	Reaction with Water
A	659	2447	900	2.7	0.41	none
B	1083	2582	390	8.9	0.64	none
C	1539	2887	470	7.9	0.11	slight
D	328	1751	130	11.3	0.05	none
E	98	890	1222	0.97	0.20	very reactive
F	183	2500	130	7.3	0.66	none
G	1063	2707	129	19.3	0.49	none
H	3377	5527	135	19.3	0.20	none

9) _Use the information above to choose a suitable metal for each of the following uses:_

☞ In all cases _explain_ your _answers:_

   a) A filament for a _household light bulb_.

   b) A metal that could be used to make _solder_.

   c) A metal used to make _aeroplanes_.

   d) A coolant for a _nuclear reactor_.

   e) An overhead _power cable_.

Plastic Structures

Properties of Plastics

1) What is a _monomer_?

2) What is a _polymer_?

3) What is _polymerisation_? _Draw_ a diagram to explain it.

4) What is a _thermosoftening_ plastic?

5) What is a _thermosetting_ plastic?

6) _Complete_ the diagram of the molecules in a thermosoftening plastic:

7) _Complete_ the diagram of the molecules in a thermosetting plastic:

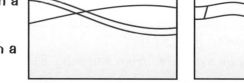

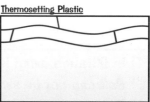

8) _Give_ the _main_ difference between the bonding of thermosetting and thermosoftening plastics.

9) _Look at the table below, which gives information about plastics._

Plastic	Cost (£/tonne)	Relative tensile strength	Relative density	Flexibility	Clarity	Thermoset/ thermosoft
A	800	1	0.9	Very flexible	Poor	Thermosoft
B	4000	10	1.1	Stiff	Good	Thermoset
C	2500	4	1.2	Fairly flexible	Excellent	Thermosoft
D	1000	10	1.4	Stiff	Poor	Thermoset
E	1600	8	1.0	Stiff	Good	Thermoset

Which plastic might be good for making the following:

> a) a fizzy drink bottle?
> b) a coat-hanger?
> c) a 13 amp plug case?
> d) the case of a transparent watch?
> e) a shopping bag?

10) What additional information might you need to choose a plastic for use on the _surface of the space shuttle_?

Top Tips: Metals and plastics, you'll be pleased to hear, show the last two types of bonding that you need to know. Remember, _metals_ have a _giant_ structure of atoms with _outer shell electrons_ floating _free_ all around the structure — which is what causes all those typical metal properties. _Plastics_ are made from very _long_ molecules, and the differences are all to do with whether or not there are _cross-links_ between them. In the Exam you can be asked about any substance and you'll have to decide what it _is_ and what sort of _bonding_ it's got — just from the physical properties. So, time to _learn and enjoy_.

SECTION TWO — CLASSIFYING MATERIALS

Separating Substances

Mixtures and Compounds

1) What is a *mixture*?

2) How is a mixture *different* from a compound?

3) State whether each of the following is an *element*, a *mixture* or a *compound*:

a) air.	d) iron oxide.	g) distilled water.
b) iron.	e) blood.	h) steel.
c) seawater.	f) common salt.	i) copper.

4) In filtration, what is a *filtrate*?

5) *Salt can not be separated from water by filtering. Explain* why.

6) How would you separate *salt* from *seawater*?

7) What is *decanting*? Give an *example* of a mixture that could be separated by decanting.

8) What is the difference between a *solute* and a *solution*?

9) How would you *separate* a solute from a solution?

10) What is *crystallisation*? Give an *example*.

11) What is a *solvent*?

12) How would you separate a *solvent* from a *solution*?

13) What does the term *immiscible* mean? Use it in a suitable sentence.

14) How could you *separate* two immiscible liquids?

15) Give *three* everyday examples of the following mixtures:

(Don't use ones that have been used before or below).

liquid/liquid	liquid/solid	solid/solid	gas/gas

16) *Give five* different examples of a filter used in everyday life.

17) Which *method* of separation would you use for each of the following?

a) To see if the red colour in rose petals was one colour or a mixture of colours.

b) To remove fine traces of sand from seawater so that they could be analysed.

c) To make sure a sample of pure copper(II) oxide was dry.

d) To obtain pure water from seawater.

e) To remove traces of yeast from home-made wine.

f) To remove chips from chip pan oil.

g) To remove alcohol (ethanol) from beer.

h) To remove lavender oils from lavender buds.

18) What could you separate using *chromatography*?

19) *Explain* briefly how chromatography works.

20) *Look at the chromatogram opposite.*

a) Out of A, B, C, D and E, which are *mixtures* and which are *pure* substances?

b) What is *C* made from?

c) What is *A* made from?

A B C D E

Separating Substances

Fractional Distillation

21) *Label* the fractional distillation apparatus:

22) *Explain* how fractional distillation can separate a mixture of liquids with different boiling points.

23) Why is fractional distillation *more efficient* at separating liquids than simple distillation?

24) *Link* the correct separation technique to each mixture below:

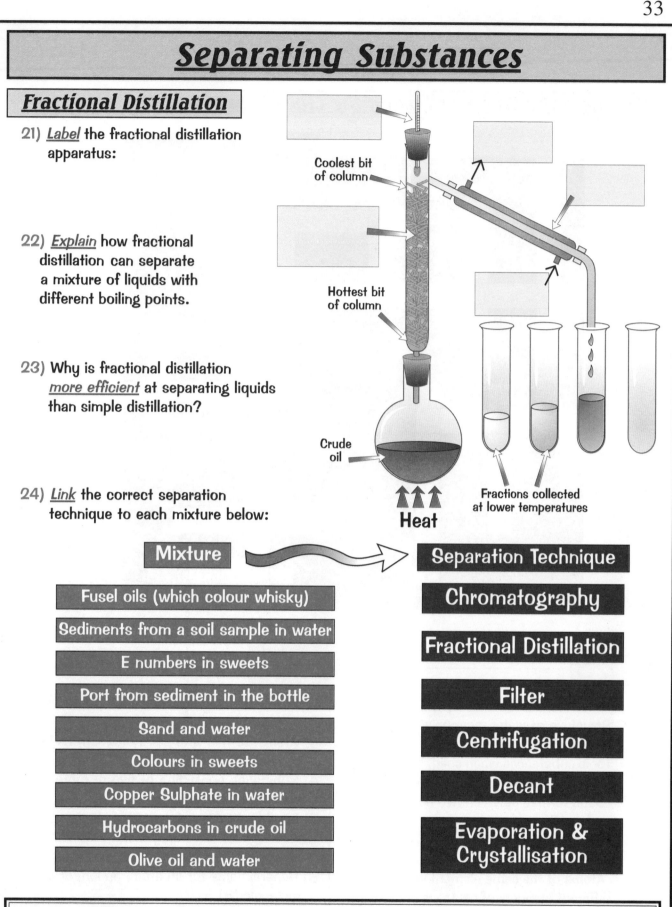

Coolest bit of column

Hottest bit of column

Crude oil

Heat

Fractions collected at lower temperatures

Mixture

Separation Technique

Fusel oils (which colour whisky)

Sediments from a soil sample in water

E numbers in sweets

Port from sediment in the bottle

Sand and water

Colours in sweets

Copper Sulphate in water

Hydrocarbons in crude oil

Olive oil and water

Chromatography

Fractional Distillation

Filter

Centrifugation

Decant

Evaporation & Crystallisation

Top Tips:
Chemicals rarely occur on their own in nature — so we need to be able to separate out the ones we want. There are *four* separation techniques you need to know, and they've all been covered on these two pages. Watch out for the *new words* — don't get confused between *solvent*, *solute* and *solution* or between a *suspension* and an *emulsion*. Remember, *separation* relies on the fact that chemicals *behave differently*, with different boiling points, melting points, solubilities or densities.

SECTION TWO — CLASSIFYING MATERIALS

A Bonding Crossword

Complete the Crossword using the Clues Below:

Across

1) Free electrons in a metal (11)
7) Structure of water, ammonia and carbon dioxide (9)
9) Ionic substances when solid, but not when in solution or molten (3-10)
10) Bond formed between two non-metals (8)
14) Subatomic particle found in shells (8)
15) Atoms of the same element with different numbers of neutrons (7)
16) Found in the Periodic Table — all their atoms are the same (7)
18) Neutral subatomic particle (7)
19) Positive particle found in the nucleus (6)

Down

2) Where an ionic substance conducts when molten, but decomposes (12)
3) Atoms do this with pairs of electrons in a covalent bond (5)
4) Substance consisting of two or more elements chemically joined (8)
5) Bond formed by exchange of electrons (5)
6) Noble gases have only these — stable electronic configuration (4,5)
8) General name for an atom, an ion, or a molecule (8)
11) Basic building block of all matter (4)
12) Bonding is determined by the ____ structure of the element (6)
13) Bond formed by metals with metals (8)
15) Charged atom or group of atoms (3)
17) Can be separated by physical means (7)

Gases

Properties of Gases

1) _Complete_ the table (you may have to think for a while about some parts, and look up others):

Name of Gas	Carbon dioxide	Oxygen	Hydrogen	Ammonia	Chlorine
Formula					
Colour					
Odour					
Souluble in water?					
% in dry air					
Does it burn?					
Will it support combustion?					
Boiling point(°C)					
Relative Molecular Mass					
More or less dense than air?					
Source of gas for commercial production					
Two major uses					
Acid or alkali in water?					

2) _Describe_ in detail how you would identify the above five gases, if they were each given to you in an unlabelled tube.

Top Tips: Admittedly, I doubt that you'd have a question in the Exam that asked for properties of all of these gases at once. But you _will_ be asked to give this kind of information for one or two of them, so, not surprisingly, you _do_ need to _know them all_. Bizarrely enough, some people still write in the Exam that "hydrogen is found in the air", which it just _isn't_ (unless you're _exceedingly_ high up). Perhaps they didn't learn this page.

Gases

Making Gases

1) _Each of the sets of apparatus on this page are used to make gases in the lab._

   For each of them, select the gas being collected from the box below, and write it _above_ the apparatus.

Hydrogen	Oxygen	Carbon dioxide
	Ammonia	Chlorine

2) Now select the correct equation for each from the box below, and write it _below_ the apparatus.

   1) $H_2SO_4 + Zn \rightarrow ZnSO_4 + H_2$
   2) $CaCO_3 + 2HCl \rightarrow CaCl_2 + CO_2 + H_2O$
   3) $2KMnO_4 + 16HCl \rightarrow 2MnCl_2 + 8H_2O + 2KCl + 5Cl_2$
   4) $2H_2O_2 \rightarrow 2H_2O + O_2$
   5) $Ca(OH)_2 + 2NH_4Cl \rightarrow CaCl_2 + 2H_2O + 2NH_3$

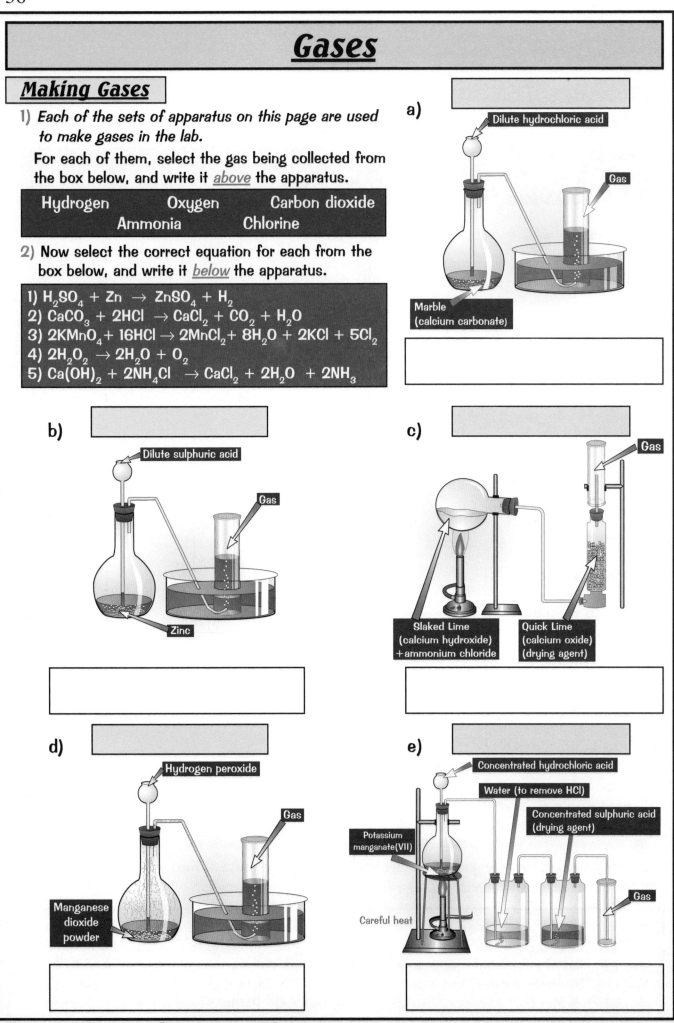

a) Dilute hydrochloric acid · Gas · Marble (calcium carbonate)

b) Dilute sulphuric acid · Gas · Zinc

c) Gas · Slaked Lime (calcium hydroxide) + ammonium chloride · Quick Lime (calcium oxide) (drying agent)

d) Hydrogen peroxide · Gas · Manganese dioxide powder

e) Concentrated hydrochloric acid · Water (to remove HCl) · Concentrated sulphuric acid (drying agent) · Potassium manganate(VII) · Careful heat · Gas

SECTION TWO — CLASSIFYING MATERIALS

Crude Oil

How Oil was Formed:

Oil and natural gas have formed from the remains of
plants and sea creatures. They are the result of the
action of heat and pressure on plant and animal remains
over millions of years, in the absence of air.

Oil and gas rise up through permeable rocks and become
trapped under impermeable rocks. They are then
extracted by drilling.

In the exploration for oil, Geologists carry out test
drilling to check for the rock formations that trap oil.

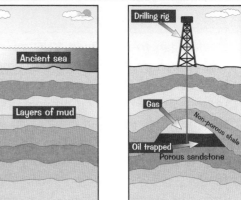

Most wells are 1000 — 5000m deep, but some can reach down 8km. Most of the oil is at high
pressure, so is easily removed. But some deposits require water to be pumped down to force
the oil out. Oil is transported in tankers or piped to a refinery where the mixture is separated.

Answer the following questions:

The Formation of Oil

1) _Explain_ in your own words how crude oil has formed.
2) _Where_ underground does crude oil collect?
3) How is it _extracted_ from the ground?
4) What does _permeable_ mean?
5) What does _impermeable_ mean?
6) What is a _Geologist_?

Extracting Oil

7) Where in _Britain_ are _oil deposits_ found?
8) Where else in the _world_ are _oil deposits_ found?
9) _Oil is a fossil fuel._ What is a _fossil fuel_?
10) What is a _mixture_?
11) Crude oil is a _mixture_ of what?
12) What is a _hydrocarbon_?
13) Why is the oil known as _"crude"_ oil?

Refining and Using Oil

14) _Why_ is crude oil of little use without refining?
15) _How_ is crude oil transported to the refinery?
16) _Name_ another method of transporting oil, not mentioned above.
17) Why are _oil spills_ a problem to the environment?
18) _Oil is non-renewable._ What does this _mean_?
19) Give three _advantages_ and three _disadvantages_ of burning oil products.

Top Tips:
All right, so crude oil isn't the most fascinating of topics, but there's a
fair old bit to learn on this page. The thing is, oil is a very important
substance — as a _fuel_ and as a _resource_ to make other useful things from. Fuel oils, plastics,
solvents and synthetic fibres all come from crude oil, which is the nasty black stuff that comes
out of the ground. You need to know _how oil formed_ in the first place, how it's _extracted_, what
it's _used for_ and what _environmental_ problems oil spillages and burning oil products cause.

Coal

How Coal is Formed:

Coal began to form over 300 million years ago.
Then much of the Earth was swamp and thick
dense forest. As this vegetation died, layer
upon layer of decaying organic matter was
formed. This changed chemically and was
compressed to form rocks.

Coal is found in seams, which are brought near
to the Earth's surface by geological changes.
Some of these seams can be mined by open-
cast methods. Other seams, which are up to

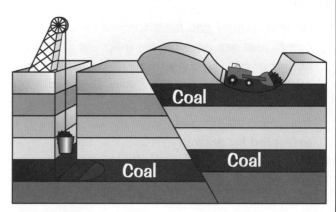

1 km below the ground, require mining by digging deep shafts.

Coal was used to produce "town gas" before natural gas was more widely used. This was
produced by destructive distillation (heating coal without air). Coal can be used to produce many
other products, such as coke, dyes, plastics, drugs, weedkillers and even TNT.

The Formation of Coal

1) What _material_ did the coal form from?
2) _How_ is coal formed?
3) What is a _seam_?

Mining of Coal

4) What is _shaft mining_?
5) What is _open-cast mining_?
6) Give three _advantages_ and three _disadvantages_ of open-cast mining.
7) Give three _advantages_ and three _disadvantages_ of shaft mining.

Distillation and Burning

8) What is _destructive distillation_?
9) What is the difference between _destructive distillation_ and _burning_?
10) Today, what is used _instead_ of town gas?
11) _Give_ two uses of coke.
12) Coke is cleaner than coal. _How_ does it still cause pollution?

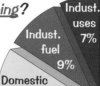

Uses of Coal

13) _Give_ six uses of coal.
14) What is _TNT_?
15) What are the _disadvantages_ of burning coal?
16) Look at the pie chart opposite.
    What is the _major use_ of coal?
17) When coal is burnt, carbon dioxide and water are released. _Name_ another oxide that is
    produced in large quantities by the combustion of coal.
18) What _problem_ does this oxide cause to the environment?

Top Tips:
Coal, it's _exciting_ — not really. But it is another starting point for
making all sorts of _useful 20th Century things_ that we can't be without,
which is why you need to know a bit about it. Just like with oil, you need to know _where_ the
coal _came from_, how we get it _out of the ground_, and what we mainly _use it for_. There'll be
some _interesting_ chemistry stuff along soon, so _learn_ this now and be _patient_.

SECTION THREE — EARTH MATERIALS

Fractional Distillation

Crude Oil and Fossil Fuels

1) What is _crude oil_?
2) What is a _hydrocarbon_? Give an example of a hydrocarbon.
3) What is a _fossil fuel_?

The Fractionating Column

4) _Complete_ the diagram below by filling in labels A to E with the correct fraction.

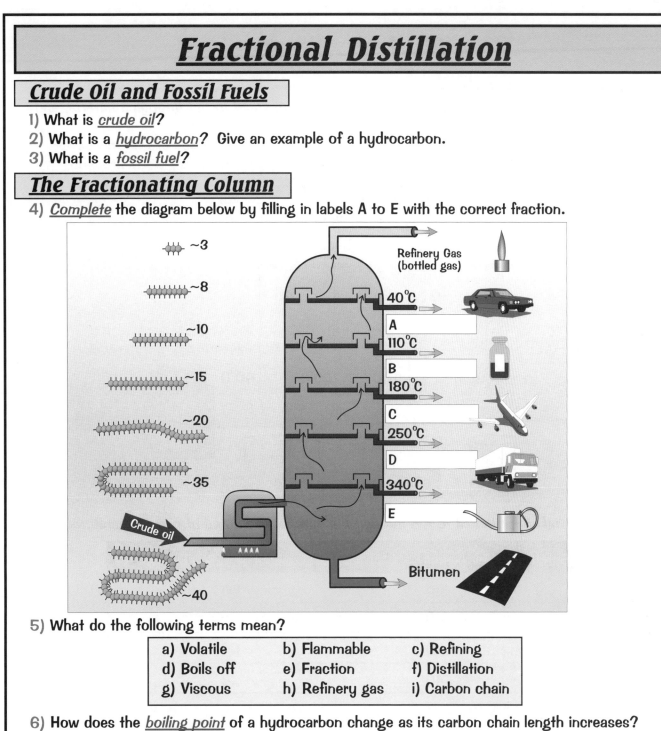

5) What do the following terms mean?

a) Volatile	b) Flammable	c) Refining
d) Boils off	e) Fraction	f) Distillation
g) Viscous	h) Refinery gas	i) Carbon chain

6) How does the _boiling point_ of a hydrocarbon change as its carbon chain length increases?
7) _Describe_ how the fractional distillation of crude oil works.
8) Why is crude oil so _important_?

Hydrocarbons

9) How does the _flammability_ of a hydrocarbon change as its carbon chain length increases?
10) How does the _volatility_ of a hydrocarbon change its carbon chain length increases?
11) Which would _flow_ more easily — a hydrocarbon composed of short carbon chains or long carbon chains?
12) Which fractions will _ignite_ most easily — short carbon chains or long carbon chains?

Finite Supplies...

13) _Oil is a finite resource._ What does _finite_ mean?
14) What could _you_ do to make oil last longer?
15) What could _all nations_ do to make oil last longer?

Hydrocarbons

If a liquid is quite "thick" and takes a long time to run down a slope, we say it is "viscous".
We can measure how long it takes for a certain amount of liquid to run through a burette, and this will indicate how viscous the liquid is.
Lubricating oils in car engines keep moving metal surfaces apart. Viscous oils do this better than runny oils; but if they are too viscous they don't lubricate the moving parts properly.

Investigation: Which Oil is the Most Viscous?

The following experiment was set up to find which of two oils was the most viscous.

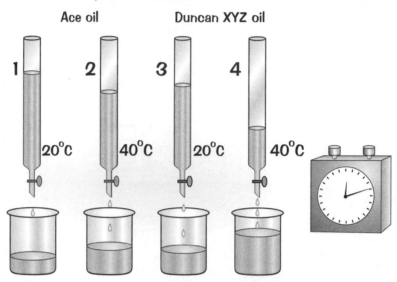

The time taken for the oil to run through the burette was noted at two temperatures.

Burette	Temperature / °C	Time for 50 cm³ of oil to flow through / s
1	20	90
2	40	53
3	20	64
4	40	28

1) _Draw a bar chart_ of the above information.
2) Which oil is _most viscous_ at 20°C?
3) Which oil is the _most viscous_ at 40°C?
4) _Temperatures in an engine are much higher than 40°C._ What will _happen_ to the viscosity of these oils at engine temperature?
5) How could you _improve_ the experiment to prove which oil was the most viscous when used in an engine?

Engine Oil and Diesel

6) If you were designing an engine oil, would you use _short_ chain or _long_ chain hydrocarbons?
7) What might happen to _very viscous_ oil on a _very cold_ morning?
8) _At one time in cold weather, lorry drivers would warm their diesel tanks by making a small fire under the tank._
   a) _Why_ do you think they did this?
   b) What _problems_ might occur doing this?
   c) _Additives_ are now put in diesel oil, but not all year round. Why aren't they _always_ put in?

Alkanes

Alkanes — Basic Facts

Alkanes are organic compounds that form a homologous series of hydrocarbons. They only contain single covalent bonds and are therefore saturated hydrocarbons. They form 3D molecules but are usually drawn flat. They have the general formula C_nH_{2n+2}. They do not decolourise bromine water and they burn cleanly to produce carbon dioxide and water.

<u>Answer</u> the following:
1) Why are alkanes called <u>*organic*</u> compounds?
2) What is a *"homologous series"*?
3) <u>*Explain*</u> what is meant by a *"single covalent bond"*.
4) What does the term *"saturated"* mean?
5) Explain why alkanes <u>*do not react*</u> with bromine water.

Combustion of Alkanes

6) <u>*Complete*</u> the following equations and balance them:

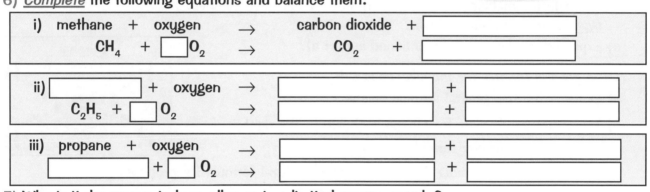

7) Why is it dangerous to burn alkanes in a limited oxygen supply?
8) Alkanes are unreactive and will not polymerise (join up to make molecules). <u>*Explain*</u>, using examples, why this is so. <u>*Name*</u> another group of organic chemicals that will not polymerise.
9) A catalyst can be used to break down long alkane molecule chains into smaller, more useful molecules. What is the <u>*name*</u> of this process?
10) Why does it make more sense to turn unreactive alkanes into <u>*more useful chemicals*</u>, rather than <u>*burn*</u> them?
11) State <u>*uses*</u> for methane, propane, butane and octane.

Methane — Natural Gas

12) Pure methane has no smell. Below are three molecules used to give methane a smell.

$CH_3CH_2 - SH$ $(CH_3)_3C - SH$ $CH_3CH_2 - S - CH_2CH_3$

<u>*Why*</u> do you think this is done?

13) A chemical with formula $(CH_3)_2CH - SH$ leaked from a university research lab in North Wales. Many local residents complained of a natural gas leak, and fishermen claimed it could be smelt at sea.

a) <u>*Explain*</u> why residents reported the smell of natural gas.
b) Why do you think fishermen could smell the gas <u>*at sea*</u>?
c) Should the gas authorities have checked <u>*all*</u> of these complaints? <u>*Explain*</u> your answer.

Top Tips:
There's plenty to know about alkanes here. But don't fret, they hardly undergo any actual reactions — <u>*combustion*</u> and <u>*cracking*</u> are the main ones. That's because they haven't got any <u>*spare bonds*</u> to do things with. You need to know the <u>*names*</u> and <u>*formulae*</u> of the alkanes in Q1, and you need to have an <u>*idea*</u> of the melting point/boiling point data.

Alkenes

Properties of Alkenes

1) *Alkenes are unsaturated hydrocarbons.*
   a) What do you understand by the term *unsaturated*?
   b) Why does this make alkenes *useful*?

2) Below is a table showing some properties of the alkenes. Use this to *answer* the questions.

Alkene	Melting Point °C	Boiling Point °C	State at RTP
Ethene	-168.9	-103.6	Gas
Propene	-185.1	-47.3	Gas
But-1-ene	-185.2	-6.2	Gas
Pent-1-ene	-138	30	Liquid

   a) Comment on any trends you can see in the:
      i) melting points   ii) boiling points   iii) states at room temperature and pressure.
   b) Estimate the melting and boiling points of the next two alkenes.
      Give reasons for your answer.
   c) Explain these trends you mentioned in part a).

3) *The general formula for the alkenes is C_nH_{2n}.*
   a) *Explain* what this general formula means.

   b) The structural formula for ethene is shown to the right.
      i) *Write* the molecular formula for ethene.

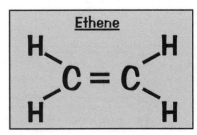
Ethene

      ii) *Propene has a formula C_3H_6. Draw* the structural formula for propene.

Addition Reactions

4) *Elements are easily added to alkenes. These reactions are called* *addition reactions*.
   a) *Why* do alkenes so readily undergo addition reactions?
   b) *Ethene can undergo an addition reaction with hydrogen.*
      i) *Write an equation* to show this reaction.
      ii) *Draw* the structural formulae of the molecules in this reaction.
      iii) What is the name of the *product* formed?

5) *The formula for the alkene, ethene, is C_2H_4.*

   a) *Complete* the dot and cross diagram of ethene to show
      the bonding (*note* $^{12}_{6}C$ and $^{1}_{1}H$):

   b) How is this molecule *different*
      from a molecule of ethane?

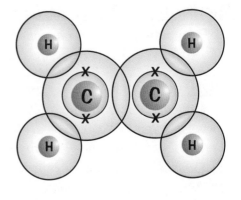

Burning with Oxygen

6) *Alkenes burn readily in oxygen.*
   a) What products would you expect from the *burning of ethene* in air?
   b) Write a *balanced* equation to show the *products formed* when ethene burns in air.
   c) *Write* a *word equation* to show what would happen when propene was burnt in air.
   d) *They tend to burn with a sooty flame. What might cause the* *soot*?

Alkenes

Distinguishing Alkenes from Alkanes

7) _Bromine water_ can be used to distinguish between ethane and ethene.

a) What happens when: i) ethene ii) ethane ...is mixed with bromine water?

b) _Write a word equation_ to show what happens when ethene and bromine water react (assume Br_2 is the species present in bromine water).

c) _Draw_ the structural formula of the product formed in the reaction.

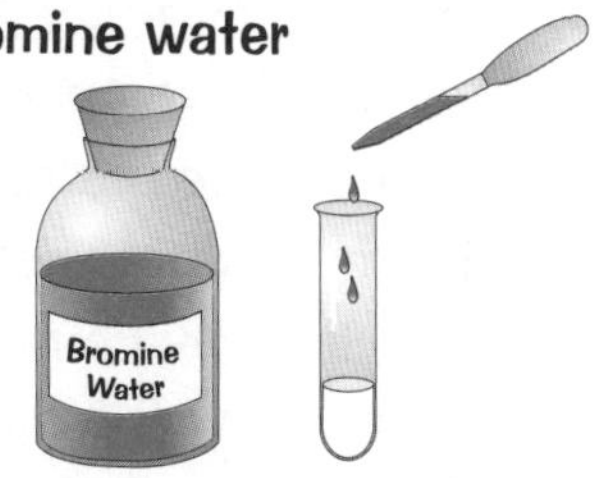

Alkene Formulae

8) _Complete_ the table below.

Alkene	No. of Carbon atoms	Formula	Structural Formula
Butene			
Pentene			
Hexene			
Heptene			

Questions on Ethene

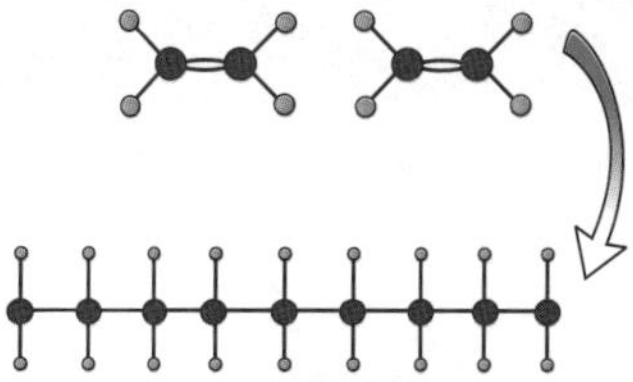

9) _Ethene is referred to as a monomer._

a) What do you understand by the term _"monomer"_?

b) Ethene molecules add together to form a very long chain. What is this reaction called?

10) _"Ethene is a product of crude oil."_

a) Is this statement true or false? _Give reasons_ for your answer.

b) Why is ethene so important industrially?

Equations Involving Alkenes

11) Complete these equations:

a) | Butene + oxygen →

b) | Butene + chlorine → dichloro_____

c) | Butene + bromine → dibromo_____

d) | Propene + oxygen →

Top Tips: Compared to alkanes, _alkenes_ are pretty _exciting_. It's very important that you remember the differences between them though. Don't forget that _bromine water_ test. Remember, alkenes are _unsaturated_ — they have double bonds, so they have some _spare bonds ready_, either to _react_ with other chemicals or to make _polymers_. Once again, you need to learn the _names_ and _structural formulae_, and you need an idea of the _physical properties_.

Polymers and Plastics

Polymerisation

1) *Explain* what you understand by the term *"polymerisation"*.
2) *Ethene can undergo many addition reactions to form long chain polymers.*
   a) What *reaction conditions* are necessary for this to happen?
   b) *Why* are these conditions needed?
3) *Lots of ethene molecules can join together to form a substance that is useful.*
   a) What is this polymer *called*?
   b) Using the ethene molecule to help you, *draw* a diagram to show how the monomers of ethene form their polymer.
   c) *Explain* the naming of ethene's polymer.
   d) Why is ethene the *starting point* for many plastics?

$$H_2C = CH_2$$

Using Polymers

4) Using the information given to the right, decide which polymer you think would be *most suitable* for the jobs below, and *fill in* the table:

Polymer	Some properties
1) Polystyrene	Cheap, easily moulded, can be expanded into foam.
2) Polythene	Cheap, strong, easy to mould.
3) Polypropene	Forms strong fibres, highly elastic.
4) PTFE	Hard, waxy, things do not stick to it.
5) Perspex	Transparent, easily moulded, does not easily shatter.

Job	Plastic	Reason
a) Hot food container		
b) Plastic bags		
c) Carpet		
d) Picnic glasses		
e) Buckets		
f) Ropes		
g) Bubble packing		
h) Insulating material		
i) Yoghurt cartons		
j) Non-stick frying pans		

5) *Monomers can join up to make polymers by two main methods: addition and condensation.* Look at the diagrams below and decide which one represents addition and which one represents condensation. (*Underline* the *correct* label).

a) $A-A=A + A-A=A + A-A=A \longrightarrow -A-A-A-A-A-A-$ (with A branches)

Addition / Condensation?

b) $A-A-A-N{H \atop H} - {O= \atop OH}A-A-A \longrightarrow A-A-A-N-A-A-A + H_2O$

Addition / Condensation?

Polymers and Plastics

Monomers and Polymers

6) _Complete_ the paragraph below by filling in the missing words.

| ethene monomers | monomer ethene | carbon | catalyst | polythene | polymerisation |
| double bond | monomer | polymer | plastics | addition | saturated | high pressure |

_____ is the formation of long chain _____ molecules from the _____ of single monomer units. The type of molecules in the _____ give the _____ its properties. _____ are made from these long chain hydrocarbons. _____ is made from the _____. _____ are brought together at _____ over a heated _____. The _____ is broken forming a _____ molecule.

7) _Other alkenes can also break their double bond to form long-chain polymers._
   For each monomer given in the table below, _draw_ what you would expect its polymer to look like, then _name_ the polymer.

Monomer	Polymer	Name
a) H $C = C$ H / H CH_3		
b) H $C = C$ H / H (benzene ring)		
c) Cl $C = C$ H / H H		

8) Sort the following into a list of the _GOOD_ and _BAD_ points of using plastics.

Fairly cheap   Can catch fire   Low density

Can be coloured   Insulators   Moulded easily

Not affected by acids or alkalis

May produce toxic gases when burnt

Non-degradable   Can be very strong   Difficult to dispose of

Top Tips: Polymerisation is _fantastically useful_ to make all sorts of plastic things. Basically, polymerisation joins up small molecules to make large polymers. Give _alkenes_ a _catalyst_ and a bit of _pressure_ and they open up their _double bonds_ and all _join up_. It's almost the opposite of cracking, but the thing is, these polymers are an awful lot _more useful_ than the hydrocarbon that they came from — and the _length_ of the polymer you get can be controlled to _tailor-make_ the molecule for a particular job. Super.

Metal Ores

Useful Products from Metal Ores

1) What is a metal _ore_?
2) _Give_ an example of a metal ore.
3) In what form are very _unreactive_ metals found in the ground?
4) _Give 3 examples_ of metals found naturally in the ground.
5) In what form are _reactive metals_ found in the ground?
6) _The diagram below shows some of the processes involved in extracting a metal from its ore._
   Match each picture a) - f) with the correct expression from the following box:

Pure metal	Carbon reduction	Earth containing ore dug from ground	Electrolysis
Metal ore detected in ground		Waste earth removed to concentrate ore	

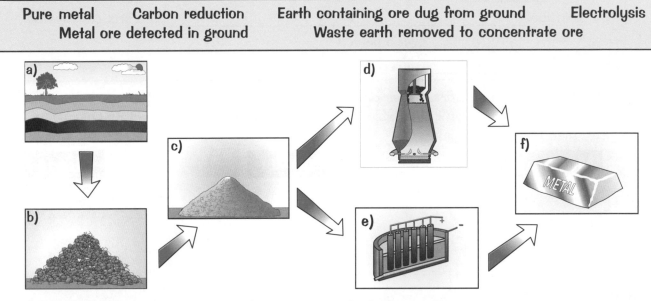

7) List each metal in the box under the correct _method of extraction_.

Thermal decomposition of ore	Reduction of metal ore with Carbon	Electrolysis of molten ore	Metals occur naturally

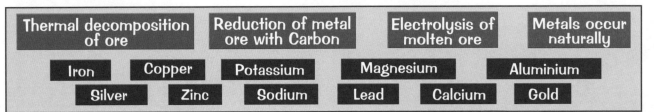

Iron   Copper   Potassium   Magnesium   Aluminium
Silver   Zinc   Sodium   Lead   Calcium   Gold

8) _Look at the table opposite._

   a) _Draw a bar chart_ showing abundance of the metals.
   b) _What does_ "abundant" mean?
   c) Which is the _most abundant_ metal listed?
   d) Name a _scarce_ metal.
   e) Was the most abundant metal the first to be _extracted_?
   f) What is the relationship between the _reactivity_ of the metal
      and the date it was first _extracted_?

Metal	Date first extracted	% Abundance in the Earth's crust
Aluminium	1827	8.1
Calcium	1808	3.6
Copper	Ancient time	<1.0
Gold	Ancient time	<1.0
Iron	Ancient time (Iron age)	5.0
Potassium	1807	2.6

9) What does the term "_native metal_" mean?

10) _When a mining company decides to start mining they must consider a number of questions:_

i) What amount of metal will be obtained annually?
ii What grade is the ore (and how much of it is there)?
iii) What will be the cost of setting up the mine?
iv) How much can they sell the metal for?

Place these points in order of importance to the mining company.

Extracting Iron — The Blast Furnace

The Blast Furnace

1) Iron can be extracted from its ore in a Blast Furnace.
   a) _Explain why_ iron can be extracted in this way, but sodium and aluminium have to be extracted by electrolysis.
   b) What is the _name_ of the most common iron ore used?
   c) What is the _iron bonded_ to in this ore?
   d) What is the _formula_ of this ore?

2) The diagram shows a section through a blast furnace.
   a) Which _three solids_ are put into the blast furnace?
   b) Why is _hot air_ blasted into the furnace?
   c) Why does the temperature need to be as hot as _1500°C_?
   d) What would you find at _A_ and _B_ in the diagram?

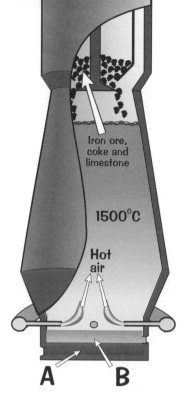

Iron ore, coke and limestone

1500°C

Hot air

A   B

Reduction of Iron Ore

3) The first stage makes the gas carbon dioxide.
   a) _Why_ is carbon dioxide produced?
   b) _Write an equation_ to show the reaction.

4) The next step: What does the _carbon dioxide_ do in the blast furnace?

5) The final step involves changing the iron oxide into iron.
   a) _Write an equation_ and balance it to show what happens.
   b) What has happened to the _iron oxide_?
   c) Write an ionic equation to show the reaction in a) (_for example: Fe^{3+} + something → etc_).
   d) i) In what _state_ is the iron at the end of the reaction?
      ii) How is it _removed_ from the blast furnace?

Removing Impurities

6) In all chemical processes it is important to remove the impurities, to leave a pure product.
   a) What is the main _impurity_ mixed with the ore?
   b) Calcium Carbonate helps to remove this impurity, but first it needs to decompose. _Complete_ the equation showing this decomposition:

   $$CaCO_3 \rightarrow \underline{\hspace{2cm}} + \underline{\hspace{2cm}}$$

   c) _Complete the equation_ showing the formation of slag:

   $$CaO + SiO_2 \rightarrow \underline{\hspace{2cm}}$$

   d) What can this _slag_ be used for?

General Questions on Extracting Iron

7) _Explain why_ use of the blast furnace makes iron cheaper than a lot of other metals.

8) Iron can exist in two forms: iron(III) and iron(II).
   Complete the table opposite showing the differences between the two forms of iron oxide.
   (Relative atomic masses: Iron = 56, Oxygen = 16)

	Iron(III) oxide	Iron(II) oxide
Formula		
Ion Formed	Fe^{3+}	
Relative formula mass of compound		

9) Give _two_ uses of iron.

10) a) _Name_ one other metal that could be extracted by reduction from its oxide by coke.
    b) _Why_ is it difficult to extract magnesium by reduction with coke?

Top Tips: Metals are all pretty useful, but they tend to occur in the ground as ores. Don't forget, the way we _extract_ them depends on _how reactive_ they are. You need to know the _blast furnace_ process for _iron_ extraction, it often comes up in the Exam.

Extracting Aluminium

Using Electrolysis to Extract Aluminium

1) Fill in the missing _arrows_ from the labels in the diagram:

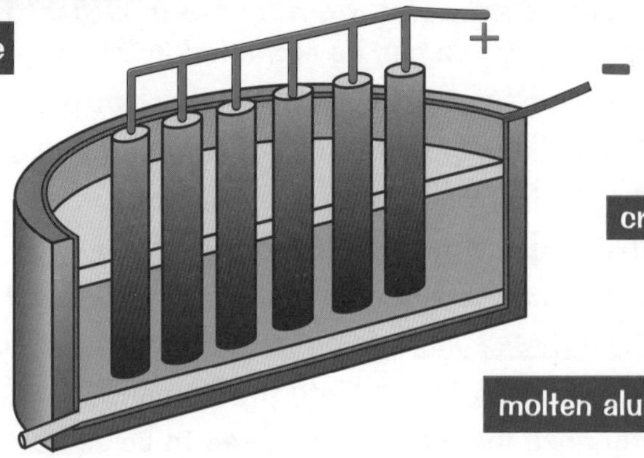

anode: graphite

bauxite in cryolite

cathode: graphite lining (carbon)

crust

molten aluminium

2) _Complete_ the sentences using the following words:

reactive	aluminium	ore	difficult	Al
O_2	bauxite	900°C		cryolite

Aluminium is much more _____ than carbon so is extracted from its _____ using electrolysis.

Aluminium is the most abundant metal in the Earth's crust, and is joined up with other elements, rock and clays, which make it _____ to extract. The ore of aluminium is called _____ which is impure aluminium oxide. It is purified, then dissolved in molten _____ (another ore of aluminium) which lowers the melting point from over 2000°C to about _____°C. Electricity passes through the melted ore separating the _____ from the oxygen.

The overall equation is: $2Al_2O_{3(l)} \rightarrow 4$_____$_{(l)} + 3$_____$_{(g)}$

Questions on Extracting Aluminium

3) Why must the bauxite be _purified_ before it undergoes electrolysis?

4) Why is _cryolite_ added?

5) _Give two reasons_ why adding cryolite is such a good idea.

6) _Write out_ the reactions that take place at the cathode and at the anode:

At the cathode (-ve):

$Al^{3+} + 3$_____ $\rightarrow$ _____

At the anode (+ve):

$2O^{2-} \rightarrow$ _____ $+ 4$_____

7) At _which_ electrode does a) Reduction b) Oxidation   ...take place?

8) _Why_ do the carbon rods have to be replaced from time to time?

9) _Write out_ a _word equation_ for the reaction that uses up the carbon of the electrode.

Extracting Aluminium

Producing Aluminium

10) *Answer these questions on producing aluminium:*

a) *Most places that mine aluminium do not smelt the metal (make it from its ore).*
   Explain why money is spent transporting ore to smelting sites, rather than smelting it where it is mined.

b) *Give an example of a cheap and convenient way to produce electricity.*

c) *Name two places in the U.K. that might be suitable for producing aluminium.*

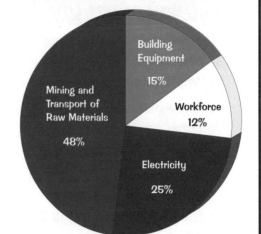

11) *A company is considering building an aluminium smelting factory near Fort George.*

   Look at the map and list five features that make it a suitable site to place an aluminium smelter.

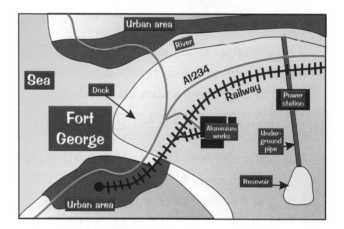

Uses of Aluminium

12) Aluminium has many uses, some are shown in the diagram below.

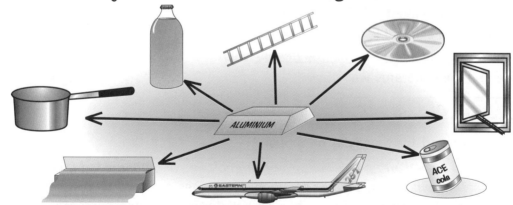

a) Put a suitable label next to each of the above uses.

b) What properties of aluminium make it suitable for the above uses?

13) *Aluminium reacts with oxygen to produce a thin layer of aluminium oxide. Why is this an advantage for aluminium?*

14) *Aluminium is not very strong, but is used widely for construction.*
   What must be done to it to improve its properties?

Top Tips: There's plenty of details here, and guess what, you've gotta know them. You need to know why *electrolysis* is used and *not reduction* with carbon — and why the *cost of electricity* is important. So, you need to understand *how electrolysis works* — and you've got to be able to label a *reduction cell*. Get it clear in your head now, and you'll be OK in the Exam. Lastly, learn aluminium's *properties* and *uses* — and don't forget why it's made into *alloys*.

Copper

Heating Copper Ore

1) The common ore of copper is a green substance.
   a) What is its *name*?
   b) What is the *chemical name* of the ore?

2) Copper carbonate can be changed into copper oxide by heating, in a process called *thermal decomposition*.
   a) What are the bubbles that appear in *tube 2*?
   b) What is left in *tube 1* after the copper carbonate is heated?
   c) What will happen to the limewater in *tube 2*? *Why?*
   d) Write a *balanced equation* for the reaction.

3) Why is copper oxide *easier* to produce from copper carbonate than magnesium oxide is to produce from magnesium carbonate?

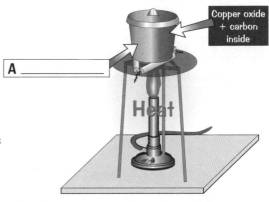

Tube 1

Limewater

$CuCO_3$

Tube 2

Heat

Bubbles of _____

Obtaining Copper by Reduction

4) Copper is obtained from copper oxide by reduction with carbon using the apparatus below.
   a) *Name* apparatus A.
   b) *Why* is A heated strongly?
   c) Why does the lid need to be *ON* when heating?
   d) *Write* an equation for the reaction.
   e) *Explain:* i) which element is being *reduced*.
                ii) which element is being *oxidised*.
   f) What would you see inside A *after the heating* was complete and the apparatus was cooled?

Copper oxide + carbon inside

A _____

Heat

The Reactivity of Copper

5) This question is about the reactivity of copper.

Copper strips were placed into a solution of sodium chloride and connected up as in the diagram below. The voltage was zero. One copper strip was replaced by magnesium and the new voltage noted. The experiment was then repeated with the magnesium strip replaced by iron and then by zinc. The results are recorded in the table below.

Metals	Voltage (V)
Copper and Magnesium	2.70
Copper and Iron	0.78
Copper and Zinc	1.10

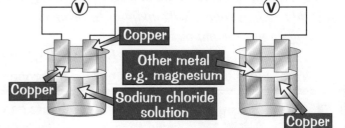

Copper

Other metal e.g. magnesium

Copper

Sodium chloride solution

Copper

From the results:

   a) Which is the *most reactive* metal out of those used?
   b) Which is the *least reactive* metal out of those used?
   c) Is there a link between the *reactivity of the metals* used and the *voltage obtained*?

Copper

Purifying Copper

Copper can be purified by electrolysis.

1) <u>Mark</u> (+) and (-) on the battery.
2) Copper metal in the impure anode becomes copper ions Cu^{2+}. Why do they travel towards the <u>cathode</u>?
3) What do the copper ions <u>accept</u> when they reach the cathode?
4) <u>Write</u> an equation to show this.
5) <u>Write</u> an equation to show what happens at the anode.

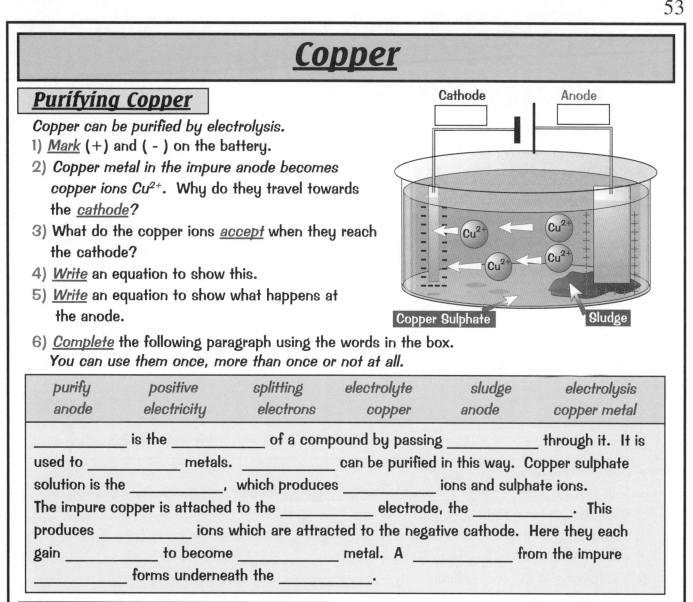

6) <u>Complete</u> the following paragraph using the words in the box. You can use them once, more than once or not at all.

| purify | positive | splitting | electrolyte | sludge | electrolysis |
| anode | electricity | electrons | copper | anode | copper metal |

_____ is the _____ of a compound by passing _____ through it. It is used to _____ metals. _____ can be purified in this way. Copper sulphate solution is the _____, which produces _____ ions and sulphate ions. The impure copper is attached to the _____ electrode, the _____. This produces _____ ions which are attracted to the negative cathode. Here they each gain _____ to become _____ metal. A _____ from the impure _____ forms underneath the _____.

Uses and Properties of Copper

7) Why is copper <u>more resistant</u> to corrosion than metals like iron?
8) Why is copper so useful for <u>electrical wiring</u> in a house?
9) <u>Give two</u> other uses of copper.
10) <u>Name two</u> alloys of copper.
11) In what <u>part</u> of the Periodic Table do you find copper?
12) Would you expect copper compounds to be <u>white</u> or <u>coloured</u>?
13) What <u>physical property</u> of copper makes it a suitable material for pans?
14) Does copper react with dilute mineral acids like hydrochloric acid or sulphuric acid? <u>Explain</u> your answer.
15) Lithium is a metal that floats on water. Does copper float on water? <u>Explain</u> your answer.

Top Tips:
Copper is a useful and important metal, and more to the point, it's on the syllabus. The important thing here is that although you <u>get</u> copper out of copper ore by <u>reduction</u>, copper is <u>purified</u> by <u>electrolysis</u>. If you learn the diagram and all the information in Question 1 on this page — remember <u>which</u> electrode the <u>impure copper</u> is — you'll be all set to get <u>loads of juicy marks</u>.

Uses of Metals

Choosing the Right Metal for the Job

1)

> People who badly break a leg or an ankle often have a pin placed in their leg to help the bones heal — they hold the bones in place and add strength to them while they are healing.

The table below lists some materials that could be used as a pin.

Material	Strength	Reactivity	Cost	Hardness	Density	Toughness
Titanium	H	L	H	H	H	H
Mild Steel	H	H	L	H	H	H
Aluminium	M	M	M	M	M	M
Ceramic	VH	L	L	VH	L	L

L = Low   M = Medium   H = High   VH = Very High

a) Does the pin need to be *strong*?
b) Just looking at the strength column — *which example* would you choose for a pin?
c) Does the pin need to be *reactive*?
d) Just looking at the reactivity column — *which example* would you choose for a pin?
e) Does the pin need to be *cheap*?
f) Just looking at the cost column — *which example* would you choose for a pin?
g) Does the pin need to be *hard*?
h) Just looking at the hardness column — *which example* would you choose for a pin?
i) Does the pin need to be *dense*?
j) Just looking at the density column — *which example* would you choose for a pin?
k) After examining *ALL* of the information, *explain* in as much detail as possible which material you would choose for a pin to place in broken bones.

Aircraft Bodies

2) Look at the information in the table below. R, S, T, and U are all metals. *Explain* in as much detail as possible which material would be most suitable to use to build an *aeroplane body*.

Material	Strength	Cost (£)	Density (g/cm³)	Melting Point (°C)
R	High	100	3.0	1000
S	Medium	90.0	9.0	150
T	High	450	8.0	1200
U	Low	200	11.0	1070

Uses of Metals

Properties and Uses of Metals

3) *The table below lists many properties of metals.* _Complete the table_ *by filling in for each property two appropriate* _examples_, *an* _exception_, *and a* _use_. *One has been done for you.*

Property (Quality)	Give two examples	Give an exception to rule (if possible)	What is this quality useful for?
Metals are solid	Iron Copper	Mercury	Used in the construction of buildings
Metals are hard			
Metals are strong (have high tensile strength)			
Metals are shiny			
Metals bend			
Metals are tough (difficult to break)			
Metals usually feel cold (conduct heat well)			
Metals conduct electricity well			
Metals are dense (heavy for their size)			
Some metals are magnetic (are attracted to magnetic poles)			
Metals are sonorous (make a nice noise when struck)			
Metals expand when heated			
Metals react with the oxygen in the air			
Metals react with acids			

Top Tips: You'll know that most of these properties are down to the special _metallic bond_ (_do_ feel free to look back at Section Two). Now you've got to make sure you can _list_ all of those metallic properties and say _why_ they're useful. Questions where you have to _choose_ a metal for a job (like those on P.54) are very common. So, _learn those properties_.

Limestone

Limestone Deposits

1) What is the main substance in *limestone*?
2) What *type of rock* is it?
3) *Name two* other rocks similar in chemical composition to limestone.
4) *Name three* areas shown on the map where there are carbonate deposits.
5) *How* has limestone formed?
6) How do we *remove* limestone from the ground?

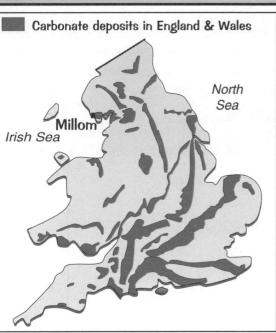

■ Carbonate deposits in England & Wales

North Sea

Millom

Irish Sea

Uses of Limestone

7) Why is limestone used as a *building material*?
8) Why is limestone used as *road stone*?
9) When limestone is heated with sand and sodium carbonate it makes which *important material*?
10) What new material is formed when limestone is heated with *clay*?
11) The material in Q10 can be mixed with gravel. Give the *name* of this mixture and a *use* for it.
12) *Mortar is a mixture of calcium hydroxide, sand and water. When the water dries out, the calcium hydroxide reacts with carbon dioxide to make calcium carbonate.*
    What *use* does it have?
13) *Finely ground limestone is used to neutralise acidic soil.* How does it *neutralise* the soil?
14) Why do farmers and gardeners often want to *neutralise* soils?

Decomposing Limestone in the Rotary Kiln

15) *Limestone is heated on a large scale in rotary kilns like the one shown below. When limestone is heated it decomposes to form calcium oxide.*

a) What does *decomposition* mean?
b) Give another name for *calcium oxide*.
c) *Describe* what you see when limestone is heated very strongly.
d) *What* do you think the expression *"in the limelight"* has to do with limestone?

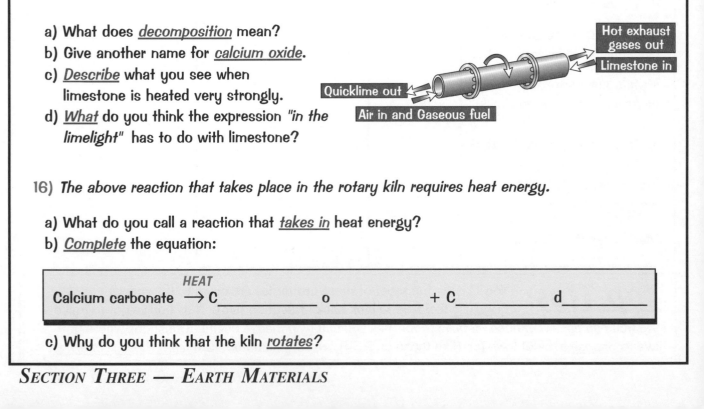

Hot exhaust gases out

Limestone in

Quicklime out

Air in and Gaseous fuel

16) *The above reaction that takes place in the rotary kiln requires heat energy.*

a) What do you call a reaction that *takes in* heat energy?
b) *Complete* the equation:

> HEAT
> Calcium carbonate → C_____ o_____ + C_____ d_____

c) Why do you think that the kiln *rotates*?

Limestone

More Questions on Limestone

17) *Calcium hydroxide forms when water is added to calcium oxide.*
Give *another name* for calcium hydroxide.

18) *Calcium hydroxide is also used to neutralise farm land.* What *kind of substance* is calcium hydroxide?

19) *Complete* the equation:

Sulphuric acid + Calcium carbonate → C_____ s_____ + W____ + C____ d_____
(from acid rain)

20) Why is the above reaction *damaging* to limestone buildings?

21) *Limestone is used in the blast furnace, which is used to extract metals like iron.* *What job* does it do in this extraction process?

Limestone Word-Search:

22) *Search* for the following words. Unfortunately some letters are missing, so *fill* those in first and then *search for the word* in the word-search.

Buil_ing
Ce_ent
Chal_
Cla_
Con_rete
_lass
Kil_
_imelight
_ar_le
_ortar
N_utra_ise
_uickl_me
Roa_stone
S_a_edlime
_oda

N	D	J	I	L	V	A	W	D	L	N	M	Y	I
E	H	K	E	A	G	O	T	E	I	D	G	D	Z
U	Q	T	I	V	O	N	S	N	U	F	C	O	K
T	H	G	I	L	E	M	I	L	K	C	I	U	Q
R	W	E	L	M	N	M	I	D	V	D	Q	U	I
A	J	O	E	G	O	R	Y	A	L	C	A	M	S
L	V	C	W	R	T	I	M	H	P	I	E	O	H
I	C	H	T	E	S	T	G	N	P	T	U	A	I
S	L	A	K	E	D	L	I	M	E	L	R	B	D
E	R	L	D	T	A	U	E	R	A	P	L	E	I
D	C	K	S	S	O	D	C	Q	N	R	M	P	E
K	T	U	S	I	R	N	O	S	E	G	B	C	E
W	A	Q	L	H	O	W	P	S	I	N	J	L	Y
S	O	P	E	C	N	T	S	I	Z	C	T	A	E

Top Tips: Limestone rock isn't just for building with after all. Well I never. Remember that limestone is mainly *calcium carbonate*. You've got to know *what* gets done to the limestone to make *calcium oxide* and *calcium hydroxide*. Of course, you need to have some idea of what these are used *for*. Don't forget that other substances react with limestone to make even more useful products like *cement* and *glass*.

Ammonia and Fertilisers

The Haber Process

1) Why is the Haber Process _so important_?

2) _The two gases used to make ammonia in the Haber Process are hydrogen and nitrogen._

   a) _Where_ does the nitrogen come from?

   b) _Where_ does the hydrogen come from?

3) _Look at the diagram opposite._

   a) Why is the iron catalyst on _large trays_?

   b) How does this _affect_ the reaction?

   c) What is the _function_ of the condenser?

   d) Why is the reaction at a temperature of _450°C_ and a pressure of _200_ atmospheres?

   e) How would a _very low temperature_ affect the rate of this reaction?

   f) | Nitrogen + Hydrogen $\rightleftharpoons$ Ammonia. |

      i) Write this equation in _symbols_ and balance it.

      ii) What does the symbol " $\rightleftharpoons$ " mean?

   g) _Not all the nitrogen and hydrogen that enter end up as Ammonia. Why_ is this and _how_ is it compensated for?

H₂ and N₂ gases

Trays of iron catalyst

Unreacted N₂ and H₂

Condenser

Liquid Ammonia

Pressure 200 atmospheres
Temperature 450 °C
Catalyst iron

Ammonia Production

4) _The production of ammonia on an industrial scale needs to be economical. The temperature and pressure can be chosen to maximise the yield._ Explain why the reaction is _NOT_ carried out at even _higher pressures_ when this would increase the yield more.

5) _Complete_ the following paragraphs by filling in the missing words from the list below. _The words may be used once, more than once or not at all._

| 450 | 1000 | ammonia | molecule | hydrogen | nitrogen | molecules |
| 200 | fertilisers | unreacted | Haber Process | recycled | pressure |

_____ is manufactured by the _____ _____. One use for ammonia is in the making of _____. The gases _____ and _____ are brought together under the special conditions of _____°C and a _____ of _____ atmospheres. Nothing is wasted — any _____ hydrogen and nitrogen is _____. Hydrogen and nitrogen combine in a ratio of 3 _____ of _____ to 1 _____ of _____.

6) _In the production of ammonia, the yield increases as the pressure is increased. However, at a given pressure — the lower the temperature, the greater the yield._

   a) Using the data given in the table opposite, plot a _graph_ of the variation of yield with pressure when the temperature is kept at 450°C.

   b) On the graph, _sketch a second line_ showing the yields of ammonia you would expect at 350°C.

   c) Why is a _lower temperature_ not used in ammonia production?

Pressure of reaction at 450°C (atm)	Approx. yield of ammonia (% volume)
100	10
200	25
300	40
400	45

Ammonia and Fertilisers

The Reaction to Form Ammonia

1) The reaction that produces ammonia is as follows:

$$Nitrogen + Hydrogen \rightleftharpoons Ammonia$$

$$N_2 + 3H_2 \rightleftharpoons 2NH_3$$

a) This reaction is _exothermic_. What does this mean?

b) If you _increase the pressure_, what will happen to the yield of ammonia?

c) If the temperature is raised, the yield of ammonia is decreased, but the rate of reaction is much higher. _Why is this_?

d) The temperature in this industrial process is chosen to be high, although the yield is lower than it could be at a lower temperature. _Explain_ why such a high temperature is chosen.

e) A high pressure will give an increased yield and an increase in the rate of reaction. _Explain_ this statement in terms of particles, gases and the collision theory.

f) Iron is the catalyst used in this reaction. Why is it so _important_ to have a catalyst?

Three Stages to Make Ammonia into Fertilisers

2) Ammonia is made into fertilisers in three main stages. Firstly, the ammonia needs to be converted into nitric acid.

Step 1

$$NH_{3(g)} + 5O_{2(g)} \xrightarrow{Pt} 4NO_{(g)} + H_2O_{(l)}$$

a) _Balance_ this equation and state the _products_ made in the reaction.

b) Ammonia reacts with oxygen as shown in this equation above. What conditions are needed?

Step 2

c) _Balance_ the equation. $NO_{(g)} + 3O_{2\ (g)} + H_2O_{(g)} \rightarrow HNO_{3(aq)}$

d) Name the _product_ formed in this reaction.

Step 3

Nitric acid then needs to be converted into ammonium nitrate.

e) What _type_ of reaction is this?

f) _Write_ a word equation and a balanced symbol equation for this reaction.

g) Ammonium nitrate is a fertiliser. Which _element_ in ammonium nitrate is particularly useful for plants?

h) What do plants _use_ this element for?

Top Tips: The _Haber process_ is something you've just gotta _learn_. Remember, it's a _reversible reaction_ — you need to know the factors that improve the _rate of reaction_ and the _yield_. Don't forget, yield and rate of reaction aren't the same and they're favoured by different factors, so the _industrial conditions_ are a _compromise_. Now once you've got your _lovely ammonia_, you can use it to make even lovelier _fertiliser_. The equations on this page are rather _boring_, but you do need to know them, so go through them _carefully_.

SECTION THREE — EARTH MATERIALS

Ammonia and Fertilisers

The Nitrogen Cycle

3) The production of ammonium nitrate is an important part of the nitrogen cycle. _Fill in_ the missing parts of the cycle in the simplified diagram below.

a) Plant protein

b) Nitrates in the soil

c) Denitrifying bacteria in the soil

d) Nitrogen in the atmosphere

e) Haber Process

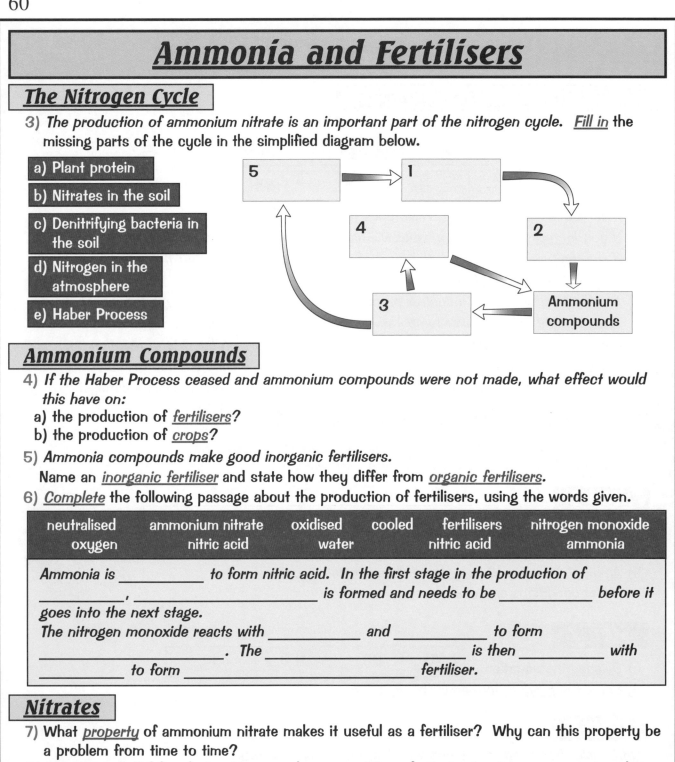

Ammonium Compounds

4) If the Haber Process ceased and ammonium compounds were not made, what effect would this have on:
a) the production of _fertilisers_?
b) the production of _crops_?

5) Ammonia compounds make good inorganic fertilisers.
Name an _inorganic fertiliser_ and state how they differ from _organic fertilisers_.

6) _Complete_ the following passage about the production of fertilisers, using the words given.

neutralised	ammonium nitrate	oxidised	cooled	fertilisers	nitrogen monoxide
oxygen	nitric acid	water		nitric acid	ammonia

Ammonia is _____ to form nitric acid. In the first stage in the production of _____, _____ is formed and needs to be _____ before it goes into the next stage.
The nitrogen monoxide reacts with _____ and _____ to form _____. The _____ is then _____ with _____ to form _____ fertiliser.

Nitrates

7) What _property_ of ammonium nitrate makes it useful as a fertiliser? Why can this property be a problem from time to time?

8) Nitrates are vital for plants. However, large quantities of nitrates in streams can cause algae and plants to grow out of control, which can eventually starve the stream, leading to death and decay.
a) What _microbes_ are needed for decay to occur?
b) What _element_ in the river does the decay process use up, and how will this affect the fish?
c) What is the _name_ given to this whole process?
d) In your own words _explain why_ nitrates cause the plants and algae to grow and why eventually this causes death.
e) How can _farmers_ help to prevent all this happening?
f) How can _nitrates_ in rivers affect humans?

Top Tips: Fertilisers are needed to provide important _nutrients_ for _plants_, particularly food crops. Don't forget the ways that nitrate fertilisers can _pollute_ the water, and what farmers can do to _reduce_ this problem. You need to know the _nitrogen cycle_, too.

SECTION THREE — EARTH MATERIALS

Redox Reactions

Reduction and Oxidation

1) *Describe* reduction and oxidation in terms of the gain or loss of oxygen.

2) *Describe* reduction and oxidation in terms of the gain or loss of hydrogen.

3) *Describe* reduction and oxidation in terms of the gain or loss of electrons.

4) What does *"OIL RIG"* stand for in relation to redox reactions?

5) *Copy* each of the equations below, adding the names under the chemical formulae. Then *mark with arrows* the oxidation and reduction processes as shown to the right:

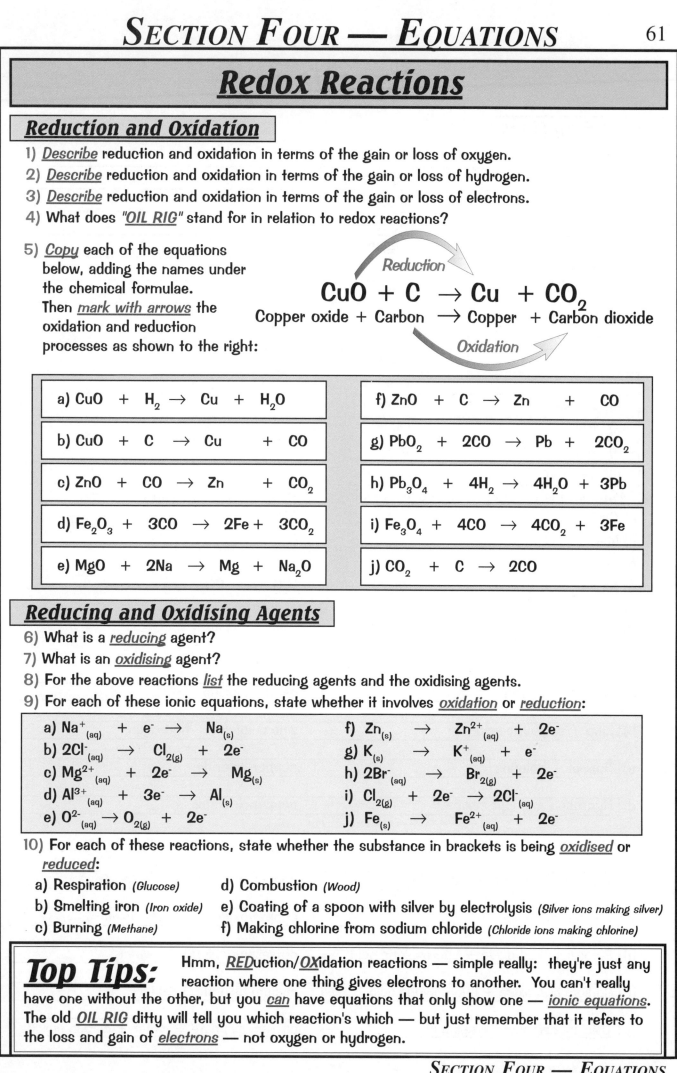

Reduction

$$CuO + C \rightarrow Cu + CO_2$$
Copper oxide + Carbon $\rightarrow$ Copper + Carbon dioxide

Oxidation

a) $CuO + H_2 \rightarrow Cu + H_2O$
b) $CuO + C \rightarrow Cu + CO$
c) $ZnO + CO \rightarrow Zn + CO_2$
d) $Fe_2O_3 + 3CO \rightarrow 2Fe + 3CO_2$
e) $MgO + 2Na \rightarrow Mg + Na_2O$

f) $ZnO + C \rightarrow Zn + CO$
g) $PbO_2 + 2CO \rightarrow Pb + 2CO_2$
h) $Pb_3O_4 + 4H_2 \rightarrow 4H_2O + 3Pb$
i) $Fe_3O_4 + 4CO \rightarrow 4CO_2 + 3Fe$
j) $CO_2 + C \rightarrow 2CO$

Reducing and Oxidising Agents

6) What is a *reducing* agent?

7) What is an *oxidising* agent?

8) For the above reactions *list* the reducing agents and the oxidising agents.

9) For each of these ionic equations, state whether it involves *oxidation* or *reduction*:

a) $Na^+_{(aq)} + e^- \rightarrow Na_{(s)}$

b) $2Cl^-_{(aq)} \rightarrow Cl_{2(g)} + 2e^-$

c) $Mg^{2+}_{(aq)} + 2e^- \rightarrow Mg_{(s)}$

d) $Al^{3+}_{(aq)} + 3e^- \rightarrow Al_{(s)}$

e) $O^{2-}_{(aq)} \rightarrow O_{2(g)} + 2e^-$

f) $Zn_{(s)} \rightarrow Zn^{2+}_{(aq)} + 2e^-$

g) $K_{(s)} \rightarrow K^+_{(aq)} + e^-$

h) $2Br^-_{(aq)} \rightarrow Br_{2(g)} + 2e^-$

i) $Cl_{2(g)} + 2e^- \rightarrow 2Cl^-_{(aq)}$

j) $Fe_{(s)} \rightarrow Fe^{2+}_{(aq)} + 2e^-$

10) For each of these reactions, state whether the substance in brackets is being *oxidised* or *reduced*:

a) Respiration *(Glucose)*

b) Smelting iron *(Iron oxide)*

c) Burning *(Methane)*

d) Combustion *(Wood)*

e) Coating of a spoon with silver by electrolysis *(Silver ions making silver)*

f) Making chlorine from sodium chloride *(Chloride ions making chlorine)*

Top Tips:

Hmm, *RED*uction/*OX*idation reactions — simple really: they're just any reaction where one thing gives electrons to another. You can't really have one without the other, but you *can* have equations that only show one — *ionic equations*. The old *OIL RIG* ditty will tell you which reaction's which — but just remember that it refers to the loss and gain of *electrons* — not oxygen or hydrogen.

62

Equations

Word Equations

1) *Complete* the following *word* equations:

a)	Iron	+	sulphur	→	
b)	Iron	+	oxygen	→	
c)	Magnesium	+	oxygen	→	
d)	Sulphur	+	oxygen	→	
e)	Hydrogen	+	oxygen	→	
f)	Magnesium	+	sulphur	→	
g)	Aluminium	+	chlorine	→	
h)	Hydrogen	+	iodine	→	
i)	Carbon	+	oxygen	→	
j)	Iron	+	bromine	→	
k)	Potassium	+	chlorine	→	
l)	Iron	+	sulphur	→	
m)	Lead	+	oxygen	→	
n)	Calcium	+	oxygen	→	

2) *Write out* the following symbol equations in *words* (they are *not balanced*).

a) $CaCO_3$ → CaO + CO_2

b) MgO + $HCl_{(aq)}$ → $MgCl_2$ + H_2O

c) SO_2 + O_2 → SO_3

d) Na_2CO_3 + $HNO_{3(aq)}$ → $NaNO_3$ + H_2O + CO_2

e) N_2 + H_2 → NH_3

Symbol Equations

3) *Write* out the *symbol* equations below the word equations:

a) Carbon + oxygen → carbon dioxide

b) Zinc + sulphuric acid → zinc sulphate + hydrogen

c) Copper + chlorine → copper chloride

d) Hydrogen + copper oxide → copper + water

e) Magnesium + sulphuric acid → magnesium sulphate + hydrogen

f) Magnesium + copper sulphate → copper + magnesium sulphate

g) Copper carbonate → copper oxide + carbon dioxide

h) Potassium hydroxide + hydrochloric acid → potassium chloride + water

i) Sodium hydroxide + hydrochloric acid → sodium chloride + water

j) Calcium carbonate + sulphuric acid → calcium sulphate + water + carbon dioxide

Equations

Examples of Balancing Equations

1) Look at the following _equation_:

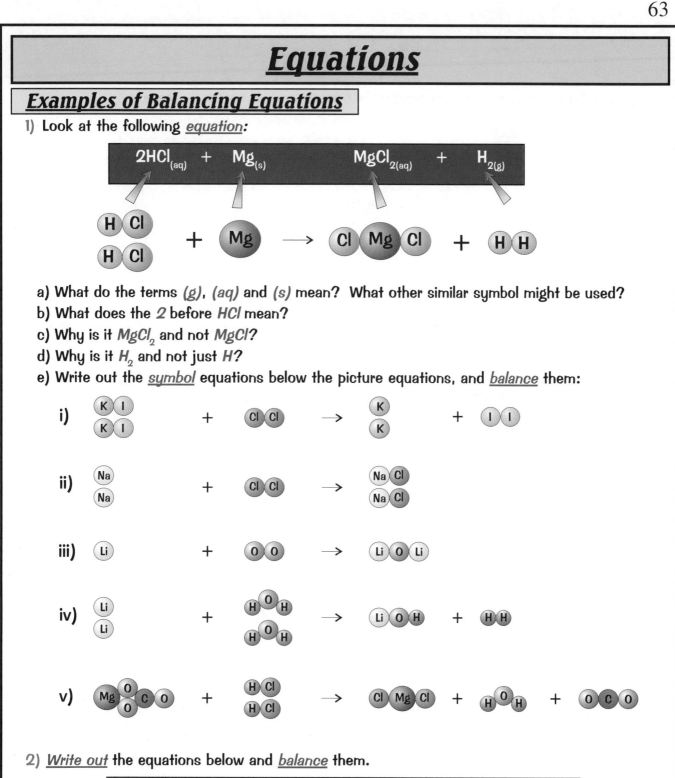

a) What do the terms _(g)_, _(aq)_ and _(s)_ mean? What other similar symbol might be used?

b) What does the _2_ before _HCl_ mean?

c) Why is it $MgCl_2$ and not $MgCl$?

d) Why is it H_2 and not just _H_?

e) Write out the _symbol_ equations below the picture equations, and _balance_ them:

2) _Write out_ the equations below and _balance_ them.

a) $CaCO_3$			$\rightarrow$	CaO	+	CO_2	
b) MgO	+	HCl	$\rightarrow$	$MgCl_2$	+	H_2O	
c) SO_2	+	O_2	$\rightarrow$	SO_3			
d) Na_2CO_3	+	HNO_3	$\rightarrow$	$NaNO_3$	+	H_2O +	CO_2
e) N_2	+	H_2	$\rightarrow$	NH_3			

Top Tips:
Balancing equations is horrible — but pretty straightforward. Once you've checked each _element_, go back and check them all _again_. Keep doing this till _nothing_ needs changing — then you'll know you've got it right. But whatever you do, don't change the numbers _inside_ the formulae — that would completely change the reaction.

Equations

1) *Balance* the following equations by putting the correct numbers before the formulae.

Easier Equations

a) N_2 + H_2 → NH_3

b) $CaCO_3$ + H_2SO_4 → $CaSO_4$ + H_2O + CO_2

c) H_2 + O_2 → H_2O

d) Mg + O_2 → MgO

e) Ca + O_2 → CaO

f) H_2 + I_2 → HI

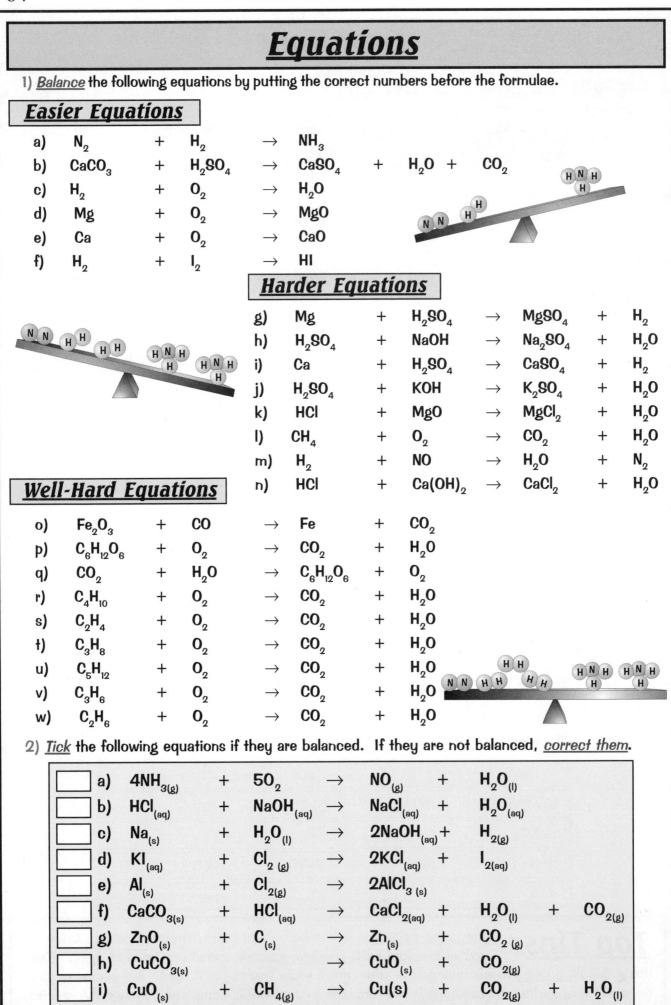

Harder Equations

g) Mg + H_2SO_4 → $MgSO_4$ + H_2

h) H_2SO_4 + $NaOH$ → Na_2SO_4 + H_2O

i) Ca + H_2SO_4 → $CaSO_4$ + H_2

j) H_2SO_4 + KOH → K_2SO_4 + H_2O

k) HCl + MgO → $MgCl_2$ + H_2O

l) CH_4 + O_2 → CO_2 + H_2O

m) H_2 + NO → H_2O + N_2

n) HCl + $Ca(OH)_2$ → $CaCl_2$ + H_2O

Well-Hard Equations

o) Fe_2O_3 + CO → Fe + CO_2

p) $C_6H_{12}O_6$ + O_2 → CO_2 + H_2O

q) CO_2 + H_2O → $C_6H_{12}O_6$ + O_2

r) C_4H_{10} + O_2 → CO_2 + H_2O

s) C_2H_4 + O_2 → CO_2 + H_2O

t) C_3H_8 + O_2 → CO_2 + H_2O

u) C_5H_{12} + O_2 → CO_2 + H_2O

v) C_3H_6 + O_2 → CO_2 + H_2O

w) C_2H_6 + O_2 → CO_2 + H_2O

2) *Tick* the following equations if they are balanced. If they are not balanced, *correct them*.

a) $4NH_{3(g)}$ + $5O_2$ → $NO_{(g)}$ + $H_2O_{(l)}$

b) $HCl_{(aq)}$ + $NaOH_{(aq)}$ → $NaCl_{(aq)}$ + $H_2O_{(aq)}$

c) $Na_{(s)}$ + $H_2O_{(l)}$ → $2NaOH_{(aq)}$ + $H_{2(g)}$

d) $KI_{(aq)}$ + $Cl_{2\,(g)}$ → $2KCl_{(aq)}$ + $I_{2(aq)}$

e) $Al_{(s)}$ + $Cl_{2(g)}$ → $2AlCl_{3\,(s)}$

f) $CaCO_{3(s)}$ + $HCl_{(aq)}$ → $CaCl_{2(aq)}$ + $H_2O_{(l)}$ + $CO_{2(g)}$

g) $ZnO_{(s)}$ + $C_{(s)}$ → $Zn_{(s)}$ + $CO_{2\,(g)}$

h) $CuCO_{3(s)}$ → $CuO_{(s)}$ + $CO_{2(g)}$

i) $CuO_{(s)}$ + $CH_{4(g)}$ → $Cu(s)$ + $CO_{2(g)}$ + $H_2O_{(l)}$

% Element in a Compound

Remember this formula:

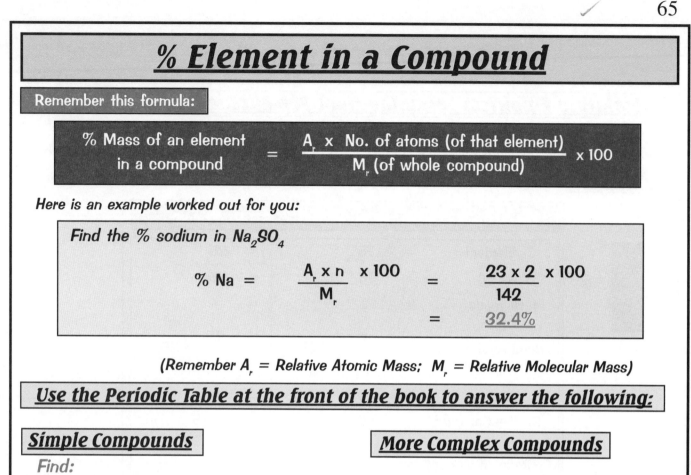

$$\text{% Mass of an element in a compound} = \frac{A_r \times \text{No. of atoms (of that element)}}{M_r \text{ (of whole compound)}} \times 100$$

Here is an example worked out for you:

Find the % sodium in Na_2SO_4

$$\text{% Na} = \frac{A_r \times n}{M_r} \times 100 = \frac{23 \times 2}{142} \times 100$$

$$= \underline{32.4\%}$$

(Remember A_r = Relative Atomic Mass; M_r = Relative Molecular Mass)

Use the Periodic Table at the front of the book to answer the following:

Simple Compounds

Find:

1) the % carbon in CO_2

2) the % carbon in CO

3) the % potassium in KCl

4) the % sodium in NaF

5) the % copper in CuO

6) the % sulphur in SO_2

7) the % oxygen in SO_2

8) the % sulphur in SO_3

9) the % oxygen in SO_3

10) the % hydrogen in H_2O

More Complex Compounds

11) the % nitrogen in NH_3

12) the % sodium in $NaOH$

13) the % water in $CuSO_4.5H_2O$

14) the % aluminium in Al_2O_3

15) the % copper in $CuCO_3$

16) the % copper in $CuSO_4$

17) the % potassium in KNO_3

18) the % phosphorus in $(NH_4)_3PO_4$

19) the % nitrogen in NH_4NO_3

20) the % nitrogen in $(NH_4)_2SO_4$

21) Which has the greater proportion of carbon?   a) CH_4 b) C_6H_6 c) C_2H_5OH
   Show how you calculated your answer.

22) Which has the greater proportion of aluminium?   a) Al_2O_3 b) Na_3AlF_6

23) Which of these iron ores has the most iron in it by percentage mass?

   a) siderite ($FeCO_3$)   b) haematite (Fe_2O_3)   c) magnetite (Fe_3O_4)   d) iron pyrite (FeS_2)

24) Calculate the proportion of metal in: a) $NaCl$ b) $MgCO_3$ c) Zn d) KOH

25) The molar mass of haemoglobin is about **33939g**. If each molecule contains two iron atoms, what percentage of the molecule is iron?

Top Tips:

These *percentages* might seem a bit involved, but its basically the *same technique* each time — so once you've got it down, you'll sail through them. Learning a few of the more common *atomic masses* will speed things up a bit — but I'd suggest using the extra time to *check your answers* — it's so easy to make mistakes.

Empirical Formulae

Calculating Empirical Formulae from Percentage Data

To find out the empirical formula for a compound you must _find the amount_ of each element and then calculate the simplest _whole number ratio_ of the amounts. Look at the example below.

Example A compound is 75% carbon and 25% hydrogen. What is its empirical formula?

Assume sample weighs 100g ☞

Elements	Carbon	Hydrogen
% Element	= 75	= 25
Mass (g)	= 75	= 25
Molar mass	= 12	= 1
Number of Moles (Amount)	$= \dfrac{75}{12} = 6.25$	$= \dfrac{25}{1} = 25$
$\dfrac{\text{Amount}}{\text{Smallest amount}}$	$= \dfrac{6.25}{6.25}$	$= \dfrac{25}{6.25}$
Ratio of amount	= 1	= 4

C_1H_4 or, better, $\boxed{CH_4}$

Two-Element Questions

1) A hydrocarbon is 80% carbon and 20% hydrogen. Find its _empirical formula_.

2) A compound was found to have 82% nitrogen and 18% hydrogen. Find its _empirical formula_.

3) An oxide of carbon was found to be 27% carbon. Find its _empirical formula_.

4) An oxide of sulphur was found to be 40% sulphur. Find its _empirical formula_.

5) Fluorspar is composed of calcium and fluorine. If 51% is calcium, _calculate_ the empirical formula.

6) Magnetite is an oxide ore of iron. If 72% is iron, what is its _empirical formula_?

Three-Element Questions

7) Cryolite is an ore of aluminium used in the extraction of aluminium from bauxite; it was found to have 33% sodium, 13% aluminium and 54% fluorine.
Work out the empirical formula.

8) Nitram is an ammonium fertiliser; it is 35% nitrogen, 5% hydrogen and 60% oxygen.
Calculate its empirical formula.

9) Saltpetre is a potassium salt; it is 13.9% nitrogen, 38.6% potassium and 47.5% oxygen.
Work out its empirical formula.

10) Caustic soda is a strong alkali containing sodium. It is 40.0% oxygen, 57.5% sodium and 2.5% hydrogen.
Calculate its empirical formula.

Empirical Formulae

Calculating Empirical Formulae from Mass Data

The method used on Page 66 uses the % of an element in a compound — but the same method can be used if the mass of an element is given. Here's an example:

Calculate the empirical formula of a compound made by combining 1.92g of magnesium with 5.68g of chlorine.

		Magnesium		Chlorine
Mass (g)	=	1.92	=	5.68
Molar mass (g)	=	24	=	35.5
Number of moles (Amount)	=	$\frac{1.92}{24} = 0.08$	=	$\frac{5.68}{35.5} = 0.16$
$\frac{Amount}{Smallest\ amount}$	=	$\frac{0.08}{0.08} = 1$	=	$\frac{0.16}{0.08} = 2$
Ratio of amounts =		1	:	2

Mg_1Cl_2 or, better, $\boxed{MgCl_2}$

Two-Element Questions

1) 2.70g of aluminium is combined with 10.65g of chlorine. What is the *empirical formula* of the new compound?

2) 1.68g of iron is combined with 0.48g of oxygen. What is the *empirical formula* of the new compound?

3) 1.6g of sulphur was heated in oxygen. Its mass increased to 4.0g. What is the *name* of this oxide of sulphur? Show how you found this out by *calculating* its empirical formula.

4) 190.5g of copper reacts with 48g of oxygen. *Calculate* the empirical formula.

5) A sample of lead chloride was found to contain 82.8g of lead and 28.4g of chlorine. What is its *empirical formula*?

6) 0.48g of magnesium is heated strongly in a crucible until it had completely reacted with the oxygen in the air. The mass of the new compound was found to be 0.80g.
   a) *Name* the new compound.
   b) Calculate the *mass* of oxygen that has been added to the magnesium.
   c) Calculate the *empirical formula*.

Three-Element Questions

7) 1.48g of a calcium compound contains 0.8g of calcium, 0.64g of oxygen and 0.04g of hydrogen. *Calculate* the empirical formula and name the compound.

8) Copper sulphate crystals contain *water of crystallisation* (water in its crystal structure) and have the formula $CuSO_4.xH_2O$, where x is a number. 49.9g of a sample of copper sulphate was found to have 18g of water of crystallisation. *Calculate* x.

Top Tips: The main thing to remember with *empirical* formulae is that they're *not* the same thing as real (*molecular*) formulae — you've got to *cancel* those numbers. So, ethene's molecular formula is C_2H_4, but its empirical formula is CH_2 — all you're doing is writing the *ratio* of the numbers of *moles* in its *simplest form*.

Relative Formula Mass

Some syllabuses might ask you to: "Find the mass of one mole of....";
others might ask you to: "Find the Relative Formula Mass of ...."

.....They're basically the same thing (but the first has grams after it).

Elements

Example Question:

Find the mass of one mole of zinc
(which is basically the same as asking....
"Find the Relative Formula Mass of Zinc")

Simply look on the periodic table (at the front of the book) for the relative atomic mass of zinc, which is 65, and add a "g" for grams.
<u>Answer</u> = <u>65g</u>

Find the mass of one mole of ....

1) calcium (Ca)	11) bromine
2) sodium (Na)	12) argon
3) iron (Fe)	13) titanium
4) copper (Cu)	14) aluminium
5) nitrogen (N)	15) gold
6) carbon (C)	16) silver
7) hydrogen (H)	17) tungsten
8) chlorine (Cl)	18) caesium
9) potassium (K)	19) mercury
10) lithium (Li)	20) lead

Molecules

Example Question:

Find the mass of one mole of zinc oxide
(which is basically the same as asking....
"Find the Relative Formula Mass of Zinc oxide")

Simply look on the Periodic Table (at the front of the book) for the relative atomic masses of zinc and oxygen (65 and 16), add them up, and then put a "g" for grams.

Zinc oxide has a formula ZnO. Which contains
$$\begin{aligned} &= (1 \times Zn) + (1 \times O) \\ &= (1 \times 65) + (1 \times 16) \\ &= \quad 65 \quad + \quad 16 \\ &= \quad \underline{81g} \end{aligned}$$

Find the Relative Formula Mass of ....

21) hydrogen molecules (H_2)	25) bromine molecules (Br_2)
22) oxygen molecules (O_2)	26) nitrogen molecules (N_2)
23) chlorine molecules (Cl_2)	27) fluorine molecules (F_2)
24) iodine molecules (I_2)	28) astatine (At_2)

Relative Formula Mass

Calculate the mass of one mole of the following....

Compounds

1) copper oxide (CuO)
2) magnesium oxide (MgO)
3) potassium iodide (KI)
4) potassium chloride (KCl)
5) hydrogen chloride (HCl)

6) sodium chloride (NaCl)
7) potassium bromide (KBr)
8) carbon monoxide (CO)
9) sodium bromide (NaBr)
10) lithium iodide (LiI)

Complex Compounds

11) copper sulphate ($CuSO_4$)
12) carbon dioxide (CO_2)
13) water (H_2O)
14) methane (CH_4)
15) ammonia (NH_3)
16) calcium chloride ($CaCl_2$)
17) ethene (C_2H_4)
18) magnesium chloride ($MgCl_2$)
19) aluminium chloride ($AlCl_3$)
20) aluminium iodide (AlI_3)

21) sulphur dioxide (SO_2)
22) copper carbonate ($CuCO_3$)
23) zinc chloride ($ZnCl_2$)
24) ethane (C_2H_6)
25) barium sulphate ($BaSO_4$)
26) nitric acid (HNO_3)
27) lead iodide (PbI_2)
28) sulphuric acid (H_2SO_4)
29) aluminium oxide (Al_2O_3)
30) potassium nitrate (KNO_3)

Hideously Complex Compounds

31) calcium carbonate ($CaCO_3$)
32) sodium carbonate (Na_2CO_3)
33) aluminium hydroxide ($Al(OH)_3$)
34) glucose ($C_6H_{12}O_6$)
35) potassium manganate (VII) ($KMnO_4$)
36) sodium sulphate (Na_2SO_4)
37) tetrachloromethane (CCl_4)
38) citric acid ($C_6H_8O_7$)
39) ethanoic acid ($C_2H_4O_2$)
40) sodium hydrogen sulphate ($NaHSO_4$)

41) ammonium hydroxide (NH_4OH)
42) ammonium nitrate (NH_4NO_3)
43) ammonium sulphate ($(NH_4)_2SO_4$)
44) ammonium phosphate ($(NH_4)_3PO_4$)
45) calcium hydroxide ($Ca(OH)_2$)
46) aluminium sulphate ($Al_2(SO_4)_3$)
47) copper nitrate ($Cu(NO_3)_2$)
48) lead nitrate ($Pb(NO_3)_2$)
49) calcium nitrate ($Ca(NO_3)_2$)
50) potassium dichromate ($K_2Cr_3O_7$)

Top Tips:

One of the trickiest things here is all the different terms. Examiners love a bit of variation — so they'll say things like *molar mass*, *relative formula mass*, or the *mass of one mole*. They're basically all the same — you work them out the same way. But just remember that if something's *relative* then it's being compared to something else, so it's *just a number* (a ratio) — it doesn't need grams after it.

Masses and Moles

Calculating the Mass from a number of Moles

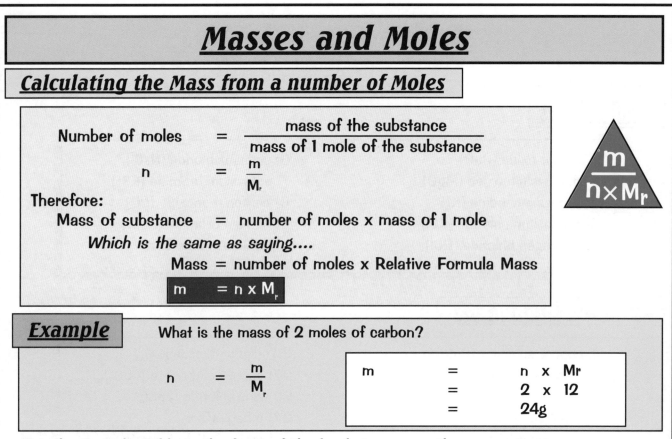

Number of moles $= \dfrac{\text{mass of the substance}}{\text{mass of 1 mole of the substance}}$

$n = \dfrac{m}{M_r}$

Therefore:

Mass of substance = number of moles x mass of 1 mole

Which is the same as saying....

Mass = number of moles x Relative Formula Mass

$m = n \times M_r$

$\dfrac{m}{n \times M_r}$

Example

What is the mass of 2 moles of carbon?

$n = \dfrac{m}{M_r}$

m	$=$	$n \times M_r$
	$=$	2×12
	$=$	$24g$

Use the Periodic Table in the front of the book to answer these questions:

1) What is the mass of...?

a) 1 mole of carbon atoms

b) 2 moles of sodium atoms

c) 2 moles of aluminium atoms

d) 3 moles of lithium atoms

e) 10 moles of iodine atoms

f) 1 mole of oxygen molecules

g) 2 moles of chlorine molecules

h) 1 mole of nitrogen molecules

i) 0.5 moles of nitrogen molecules

j) 0.1 moles of carbon molecules

2) What is the mass of...?

a) 1 mole of carbon dioxide (CO_2)

b) 5 moles of carbon dioxide (CO_2)

c) 3 moles of water (H_2O)

d) 2 moles of sulphur trioxide (SO_3)

e) 3 moles of nitric acid (HNO_3)

f) 10 moles of hydrochloric acid (HCl)

g) 100 moles of sulphuric acid (H_2SO_4)

h) 50 moles of sodium hydroxide (NaOH)

i) 30 moles of calcium oxide (CaO)

j) 25 moles of sodium chloride (NaCl)

3) What is the mass of...?

a) 0.1 moles of copper oxide (CuO)

b) 0.1 moles of calcium carbonate ($CaCO_3$)

c) 0.01 moles of sulphuric acid (H_2SO_4)

d) 0.2 moles of calcium chloride ($CaCl_2$)

e) 0.25 moles of sodium carbonate (Na_2CO_3)

f) 0.05 moles of sodium hydroxide (NaOH)

g) 0.58 moles of aluminium oxide (Al_2O_3)

h) 0.1 moles of propanoic acid (C_2H_5COOH)

i) 0.5 moles of potassium manganate(VII) ($KMnO_4$)

j) 0.25 moles of Hydrated Magnesium Sulphate
($MgSO_4.7H_2O$)

Masses and Moles

Calculating The Number of Moles from a given Mass

Number of moles $= \dfrac{\text{mass of the substance}}{\text{mass of 1 mole of the substance}}$

$n = \dfrac{m}{M_r}$

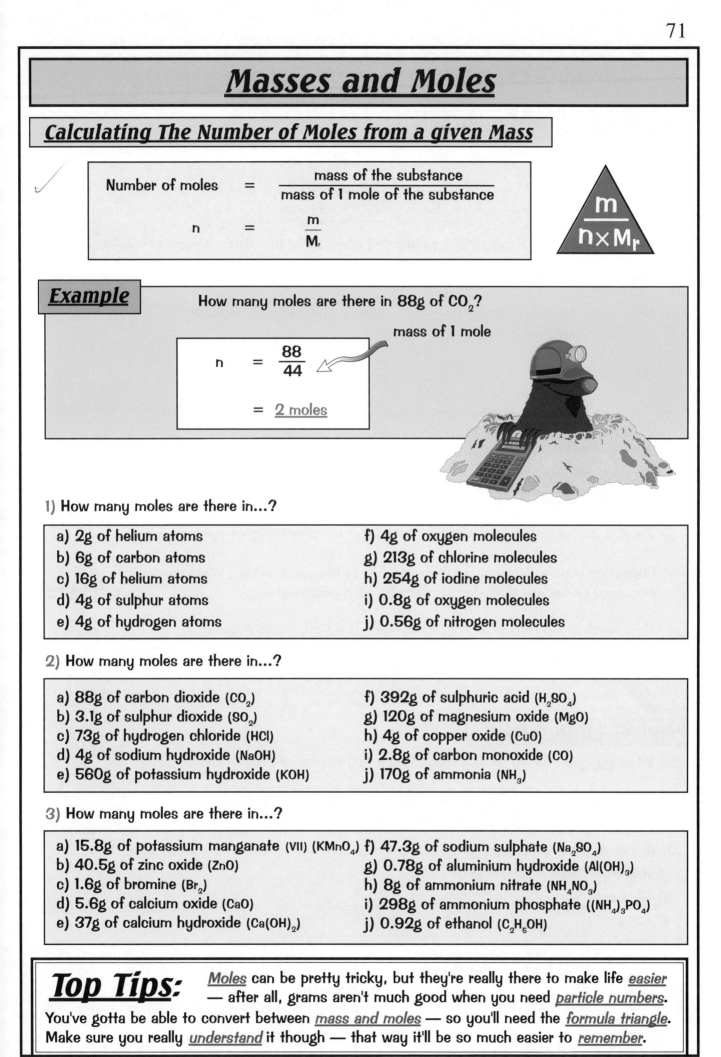

$$\dfrac{m}{n \times M_r}$$

Example

How many moles are there in 88g of CO_2?

mass of 1 mole

$$n = \dfrac{88}{44}$$

$$= \underline{2 \text{ moles}}$$

1) How many moles are there in...?

a) 2g of helium atoms
b) 6g of carbon atoms
c) 16g of helium atoms
d) 4g of sulphur atoms
e) 4g of hydrogen atoms

f) 4g of oxygen molecules
g) 213g of chlorine molecules
h) 254g of iodine molecules
i) 0.8g of oxygen molecules
j) 0.56g of nitrogen molecules

2) How many moles are there in...?

a) 88g of carbon dioxide (CO_2)
b) 3.1g of sulphur dioxide (SO_2)
c) 73g of hydrogen chloride (HCl)
d) 4g of sodium hydroxide (NaOH)
e) 560g of potassium hydroxide (KOH)

f) 392g of sulphuric acid (H_2SO_4)
g) 120g of magnesium oxide (MgO)
h) 4g of copper oxide (CuO)
i) 2.8g of carbon monoxide (CO)
j) 170g of ammonia (NH_3)

3) How many moles are there in...?

a) 15.8g of potassium manganate (VII) ($KMnO_4$)
b) 40.5g of zinc oxide (ZnO)
c) 1.6g of bromine (Br_2)
d) 5.6g of calcium oxide (CaO)
e) 37g of calcium hydroxide ($Ca(OH)_2$)

f) 47.3g of sodium sulphate (Na_2SO_4)
g) 0.78g of aluminium hydroxide ($Al(OH)_3$)
h) 8g of ammonium nitrate (NH_4NO_3)
i) 298g of ammonium phosphate (($NH_4)_3PO_4$)
j) 0.92g of ethanol (C_2H_5OH)

Top Tips:

<u>Moles</u> can be pretty tricky, but they're really there to make life <u>easier</u> — after all, grams aren't much good when you need <u>particle numbers</u>.
You've gotta be able to convert between <u>mass and moles</u> — so you'll need the <u>formula triangle</u>.
Make sure you really <u>understand</u> it though — that way it'll be so much easier to <u>remember</u>.

Reacting Amount Calculations

Reacting Amount Questions

1) *Work out* the mass of *iron sulphide* produced when 5.6g of iron completely reacts with excess sulphur.

$$Fe + S \rightarrow FeS$$

2) *Calculate* the mass of *iron sulphide* produced when 320g of sulphur is reacted with excess iron.

3) *Calculate* the mass of iron required to make 8.8g of *iron sulphide* by reacting iron with sulphur.

4) What is the mass of *magnesium oxide* produced when 48g of magnesium is oxidised in *air* to make magnesium oxide.

$$2Mg + O_2 \rightarrow 2MgO$$

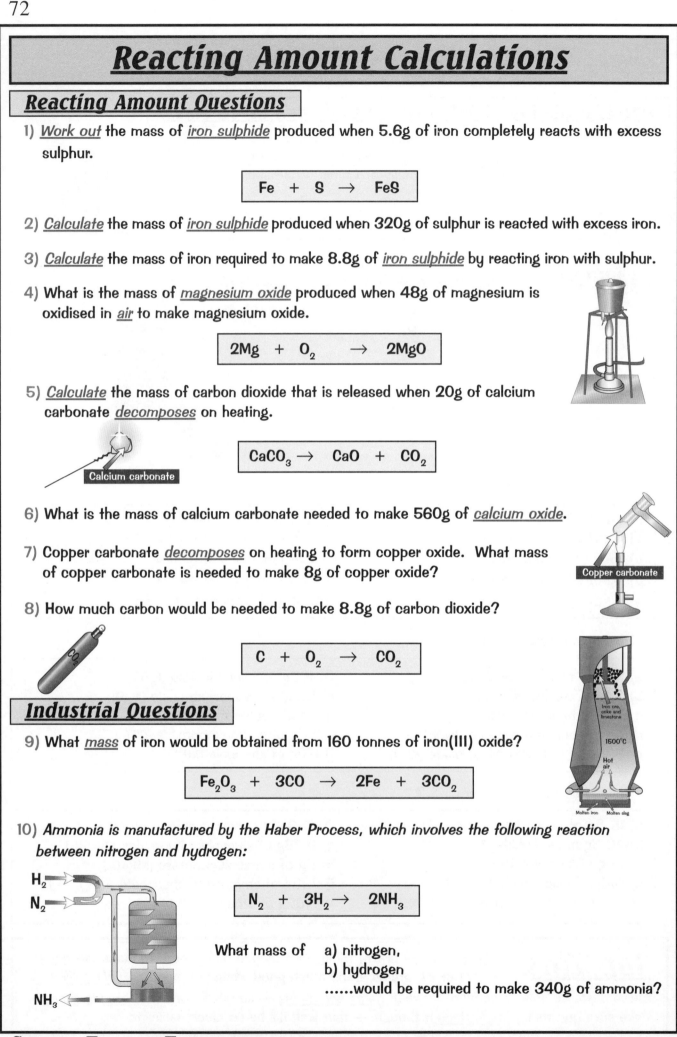

5) *Calculate* the mass of carbon dioxide that is released when 20g of calcium carbonate *decomposes* on heating.

Calcium carbonate

$$CaCO_3 \rightarrow CaO + CO_2$$

6) What is the mass of calcium carbonate needed to make 560g of *calcium oxide*.

7) Copper carbonate *decomposes* on heating to form copper oxide. What mass of copper carbonate is needed to make 8g of copper oxide?

Copper carbonate

8) How much carbon would be needed to make 8.8g of carbon dioxide?

$$C + O_2 \rightarrow CO_2$$

Industrial Questions

9) What *mass* of iron would be obtained from 160 tonnes of iron(III) oxide?

$$Fe_2O_3 + 3CO \rightarrow 2Fe + 3CO_2$$

Iron ore, coke and limestone

1500°C

Hot air

Molten iron   Molten slag

10) *Ammonia is manufactured by the Haber Process, which involves the following reaction between nitrogen and hydrogen:*

H_2
N_2

$$N_2 + 3H_2 \rightarrow 2NH_3$$

NH_3

What mass of   a) nitrogen,
               b) hydrogen
               ......would be required to make 340g of ammonia?

SECTION FOUR — EQUATIONS

Reacting Amount Calculations

General Questions

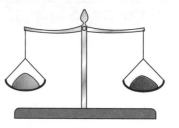

1) Which has the _greater number_ of atoms — 230g of sodium or 230g of potassium?

2) Which has the _least number_ of atoms — 5g of hydrogen gas or 10g of helium?

3) What mass of nitrogen gas has the same number of _particles_ as 320g of oxygen gas?

4) How much _anhydrous_ $CuSO_4$ is produced when 22.4g of _hydrated_ copper sulphate $(CuSO_4.5H_2O)$ is gently heated?

5) How much aluminium oxide would be needed to make the following _amounts_ of aluminium?

   a) 1kg   b) 2kg   c) 4.5kg   d) 1 tonne _(1 tonne = 1000kg)_

$$2Al_2O_3 \;\rightarrow\; 4Al \;+\; 3O_2$$

6) _Potassium chloride can be prepared by neutralising hydrochloric acid with potassium hydroxide._

   i) State the _mass_ of 1 mole of potassium hydroxide (KOH).
   ii) What _mass_ of potassium chloride (KCl) will be produced when 1 mole of potassium hydroxide reacts completely with hydrochloric acid?

$$HCl \;+\; KOH \;\rightarrow\; KCl \;+\; NaOH$$

More Difficult Questions

7) _Copper oxide can be reduced to copper using methane._ How much copper oxide would be needed to make 19.2g of copper?

$$4CuO \;+\; CH_4 \;\rightarrow\; 4Cu \;+\; CO_2 \;+\; 2H_2O$$

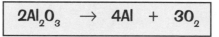

8) How much calcium oxide is produced by heating 25 tonnes of calcium carbonate?

$$CaCO_3 \;\rightarrow\; CaO \;+\; CO_2$$

9) What mass of water is produced by completely _burning_ 15kg of butane?

$$2C_4H_{10} \;+\; 13O_2 \rightarrow\; 8CO_2 \;+\; 10H_2O$$

Top Tips: These questions are really just _jazzed-up mole calculations_ — but typical Exam questions. You've got to look at an _entire equation_ instead of just one formula — but the method's basically the _same_. Don't forget in practice you'd never get quite as much product as you calculate here — there'll always be a bit left unreacted, or some gas escaping. In other words, you'll have _less than 100% yield_.

Calculating Volumes

Changing State of Matter

To answer these questions you must know that a mole of any gas at room temperature and pressure (RTP) occupies _24 litres_ (that's 24,000 cm³).

Avogadro's Law states that... "at the same temperature and pressure, equal volumes of all gases contain equal numbers of molecules".

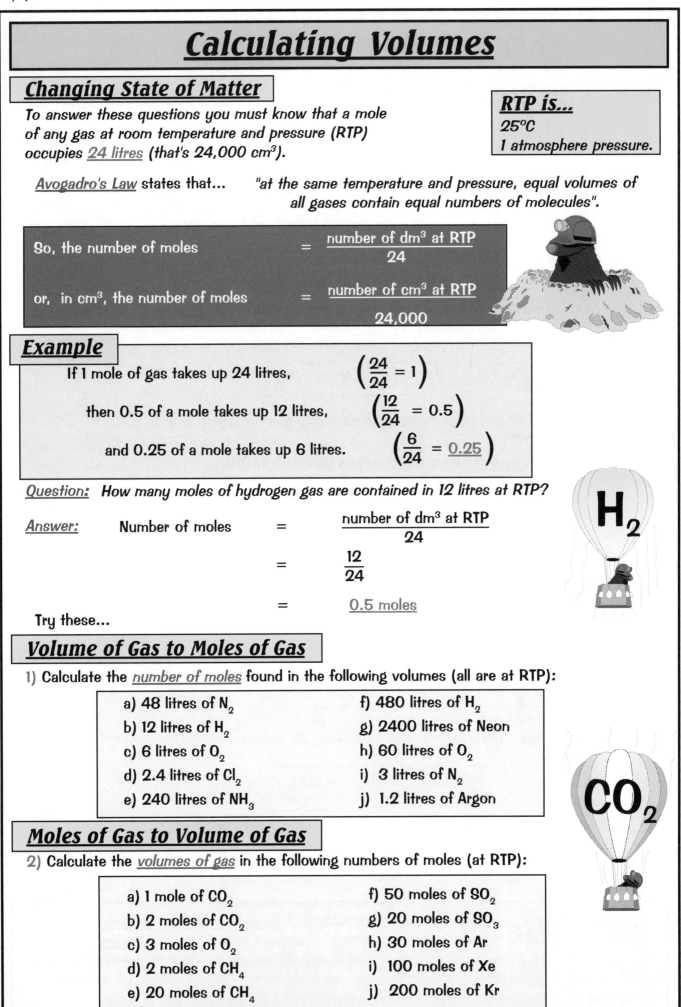

So, the number of moles $= \dfrac{\text{number of dm}^3 \text{ at RTP}}{24}$

or, in cm³, the number of moles $= \dfrac{\text{number of cm}^3 \text{ at RTP}}{24{,}000}$

Example

If 1 mole of gas takes up 24 litres, $\left(\dfrac{24}{24} = 1\right)$

then 0.5 of a mole takes up 12 litres, $\left(\dfrac{12}{24} = 0.5\right)$

and 0.25 of a mole takes up 6 litres. $\left(\dfrac{6}{24} = \underline{0.25}\right)$

Question: How many moles of hydrogen gas are contained in 12 litres at RTP?

Answer: Number of moles $= \dfrac{\text{number of dm}^3 \text{ at RTP}}{24}$

$= \dfrac{12}{24}$

$= \underline{0.5 \text{ moles}}$

Try these...

Volume of Gas to Moles of Gas

1) Calculate the _number of moles_ found in the following volumes (all are at RTP):

a) 48 litres of N_2 f) 480 litres of H_2

b) 12 litres of H_2 g) 2400 litres of Neon

c) 6 litres of O_2 h) 60 litres of O_2

d) 2.4 litres of Cl_2 i) 3 litres of N_2

e) 240 litres of NH_3 j) 1.2 litres of Argon

Moles of Gas to Volume of Gas

2) Calculate the _volumes of gas_ in the following numbers of moles (at RTP):

a) 1 mole of CO_2 f) 50 moles of SO_2

b) 2 moles of CO_2 g) 20 moles of SO_3

c) 3 moles of O_2 h) 30 moles of Ar

d) 2 moles of CH_4 i) 100 moles of Xe

e) 20 moles of CH_4 j) 200 moles of Kr

Calculating Volumes

More Moles of Gas to Volume of Gas

3) Calculate the _volume_ of the following at RTP:

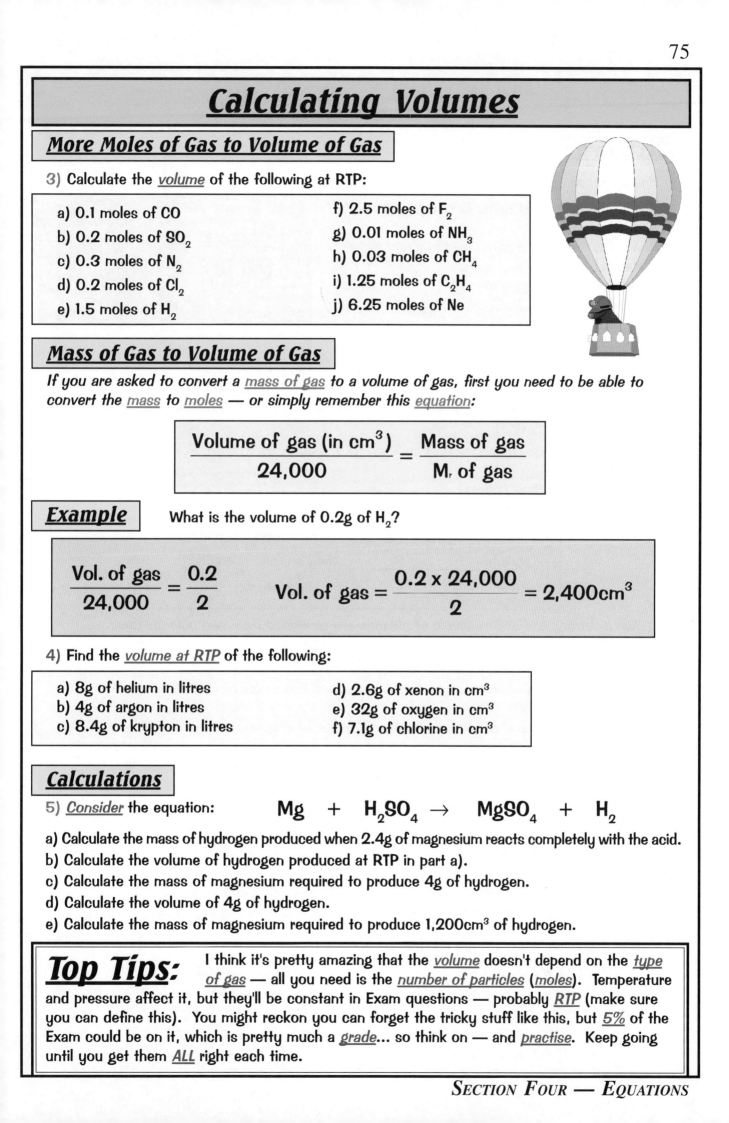

a) 0.1 moles of CO

b) 0.2 moles of SO_2

c) 0.3 moles of N_2

d) 0.2 moles of Cl_2

e) 1.5 moles of H_2

f) 2.5 moles of F_2

g) 0.01 moles of NH_3

h) 0.03 moles of CH_4

i) 1.25 moles of C_2H_4

j) 6.25 moles of Ne

Mass of Gas to Volume of Gas

If you are asked to convert a mass of gas to a volume of gas, first you need to be able to convert the mass to moles — or simply remember this equation:

$$\frac{\text{Volume of gas (in cm}^3)}{24,000} = \frac{\text{Mass of gas}}{M_r \text{ of gas}}$$

Example

What is the volume of 0.2g of H_2?

$$\frac{\text{Vol. of gas}}{24,000} = \frac{0.2}{2} \qquad \text{Vol. of gas} = \frac{0.2 \times 24,000}{2} = 2,400\text{cm}^3$$

4) Find the _volume at RTP_ of the following:

a) 8g of helium in litres

b) 4g of argon in litres

c) 8.4g of krypton in litres

d) 2.6g of xenon in cm^3

e) 32g of oxygen in cm^3

f) 7.1g of chlorine in cm^3

Calculations

5) _Consider_ the equation: $Mg \;+\; H_2SO_4 \;\rightarrow\; MgSO_4 \;+\; H_2$

a) Calculate the mass of hydrogen produced when 2.4g of magnesium reacts completely with the acid.

b) Calculate the volume of hydrogen produced at RTP in part a).

c) Calculate the mass of magnesium required to produce 4g of hydrogen.

d) Calculate the volume of 4g of hydrogen.

e) Calculate the mass of magnesium required to produce 1,200cm³ of hydrogen.

Top Tips:
I think it's pretty amazing that the _volume_ doesn't depend on the _type of gas_ — all you need is the _number of particles_ (_moles_). Temperature and pressure affect it, but they'll be constant in Exam questions — probably _RTP_ (make sure you can define this). You might reckon you can forget the tricky stuff like this, but _5%_ of the Exam could be on it, which is pretty much a _grade_... so think on — and _practise_. Keep going until you get them _ALL_ right each time.

Electrolysis

Electrolysis

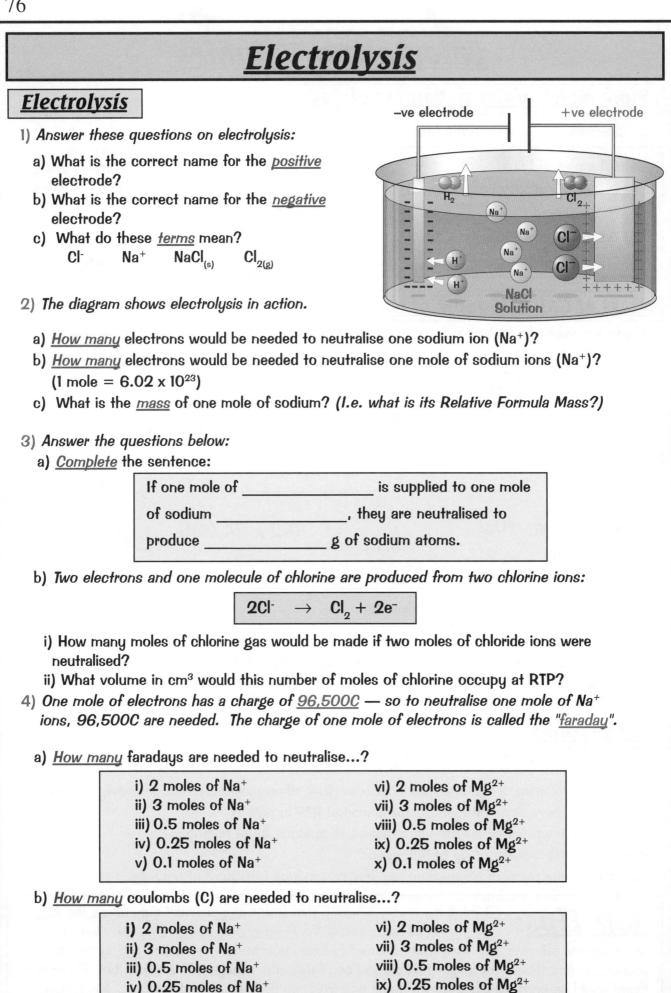

1) *Answer these questions on electrolysis:*

a) What is the correct name for the *positive* electrode?

b) What is the correct name for the *negative* electrode?

c) What do these *terms* mean?

Cl^- Na^+ $NaCl_{(s)}$ $Cl_{2(g)}$

2) *The diagram shows electrolysis in action.*

a) *How many* electrons would be needed to neutralise one sodium ion (Na^+)?

b) *How many* electrons would be needed to neutralise one mole of sodium ions (Na^+)? (1 mole = 6.02×10^{23})

c) What is the *mass* of one mole of sodium? *(I.e. what is its Relative Formula Mass?)*

3) *Answer the questions below:*

a) *Complete* the sentence:

> If one mole of _____ is supplied to one mole
>
> of sodium _____, they are neutralised to
>
> produce _____ g of sodium atoms.

b) *Two electrons and one molecule of chlorine are produced from two chlorine ions:*

$$2Cl^- \rightarrow Cl_2 + 2e^-$$

i) How many moles of chlorine gas would be made if two moles of chloride ions were neutralised?

ii) What volume in cm^3 would this number of moles of chlorine occupy at RTP?

4) *One mole of electrons has a charge of 96,500C — so to neutralise one mole of Na^+ ions, 96,500C are needed. The charge of one mole of electrons is called the "faraday".*

a) *How many* faradays are needed to neutralise...?

i) 2 moles of Na^+	vi) 2 moles of Mg^{2+}
ii) 3 moles of Na^+	vii) 3 moles of Mg^{2+}
iii) 0.5 moles of Na^+	viii) 0.5 moles of Mg^{2+}
iv) 0.25 moles of Na^+	ix) 0.25 moles of Mg^{2+}
v) 0.1 moles of Na^+	x) 0.1 moles of Mg^{2+}

b) *How many* coulombs (C) are needed to neutralise...?

i) 2 moles of Na^+	vi) 2 moles of Mg^{2+}
ii) 3 moles of Na^+	vii) 3 moles of Mg^{2+}
iii) 0.5 moles of Na^+	viii) 0.5 moles of Mg^{2+}
iv) 0.25 moles of Na^+	ix) 0.25 moles of Mg^{2+}
v) 0.1 moles of Na^+	x) 0.1 moles of Mg^{2+}

Electrolysis

Current, Charge and Time

5) In an electrolysis experiment a current of 0.1 amp was left on for an hour.

a) What is 1 hour in seconds?

b) _Calculate_ the charge Q. (use Charge = Current x Time; Q = I x t)

c) _Calculate_ the fraction of a mole of electrons that you have (1 mole = 96,500C).

d) What fraction of a mole of sodium would you have?

e) _Work out_ the mass of this many moles of sodium.

6) The diagram shows the electrolysis of brine:

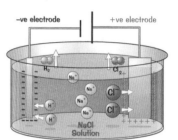

a) _Write an ionic equation_ to show what happens at:

   i) the negative electrode.

   ii) the positive electrode.

b) Which _ions_ are left behind in solution and what would this form?

c) A current of _0.05A_ is passed through the solution for _3 hours_. Assuming that this occurs at RTP (so one mole of gas occupies 24 litres), _calculate_ the volume of:

   i) hydrogen gas evolved at the electrodes

   ii) chlorine gas evolved at the electrodes

> Hints:
> 1) Charge = Current $\times$ Time (Q = I x t)
> 2) Two moles of electrons are needed for the evolution of one
>   mole of chlorine molecules and one mole of hydrogen molecules.

d) The experiment is repeated, but this time with a current of _0.075A_ that runs for _5 hours_. _Calculate_:

   i) the volume of chlorine evolved

   ii) the volume of hydrogen evolved

7) Metal items can be copper-plated by placing them in copper sulphate solution and connecting them to the cathode. Copper is deposited on them when the current flows.

a) Write an _ionic equation_ to represent what happens at the cathode.

b) What is the _mass_ of one mole of copper?

c) How many _coulombs_ would be required to deposit one mole of copper?

d) If a current of _2A_ was passed through the solution for _80 minutes_, how many coulombs would pass through the solution?

e) How many _grams_ of copper would be deposited at the cathode by this quantity of charge passing through the solution?

Top Tips:
I'd say if you can write down the _ionic equations_ for each _electrode_ then you've pretty much got your electrolysis down — assuming of course you know your _cathode_ from your _anode_. And knowing that _charge = current x time_ is pretty essential — just make sure the time's in _seconds_ (_NOT_ hours or minutes like in most Exams).

The Atmosphere

Composition of the Air

1) Copper turnings were placed in a tube connected to two gas syringes as shown in the diagram below. The air in the syringes was passed backwards and forwards over the copper as it was heated. After heating for five minutes the apparatus was allowed to cool and the volume of air left in the syringe was noted.

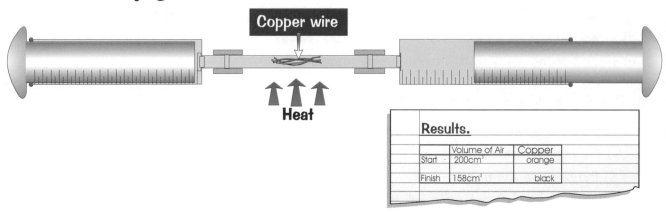

Copper wire

Heat

Results.

	Volume of Air	Copper
Start	200cm³	orange
Finish	158cm³	black

a) From the results, _calculate_ the reduction in volume of air.

b) _Work this out_ as a percentage of air.

c) What is the name of the _active component_ of air which has apparently disappeared?

d) _Where_ do you think the gas has gone?

e) _Construct_ a word equation to show exactly what has happened to the copper.

f) Why do you think the apparatus was _allowed to cool_ before a final reading was taken?

g) Name a gas _still present_ in the syringes at the end of the experiment and give a _use_ for this gas.

Burning Questions

2) The diagrams opposite show an experiment on combustion. Stephen placed a burning candle on a petri dish in a bowl of water. He then placed a bell jar over the candle, trapping 10 litres of air above the water. Stephen had expected the water level to rise, but it didn't. Eventually the candle went out, and then the water level steadily rose.

Answer the following questions:

a) What gas did the candle need in order to _burn_ properly?

b) Why do you think Stephen expected the water level to _rise_ as the candle burnt?

c) Candle wax is a hydrocarbon. Name the gaseous products of the _complete combustion_ of the candle. What other gaseous product results from _incomplete combustion_?

d) _Explain_ why the water level did not rise quickly as Stephen had expected.

e) _Explain_ why eventually the level rose once the candle had gone out.

3) The three things needed for burning are displayed in the _Fire Triangle_ opposite. _Complete_ the drawing by filling in the two missing labels.

4) Incomplete combustion can produce poisonous carbon monoxide. _What precautions_ should be taken in the home to ensure that gas appliances do not produce this gas?

The Fire Triangle

The Atmosphere

Changes in the Earth's Atmosphere

The graphs below give information about the Earth's atmosphere millions of years ago and today.

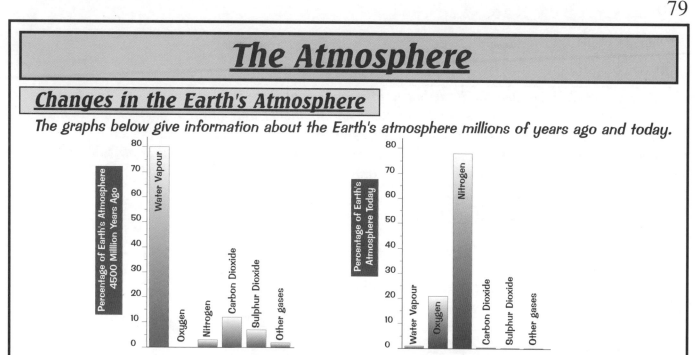

1) Could the early atmosphere _support life_ as we know it? Explain your answer.

2) _About 3,000 million years ago simple organisms started to photosynthesise._ Which gas did this remove from the early atmosphere? _Write_ a word and symbol equation for this reaction.

3) Which organisms caused the increase in oxygen and the decrease in carbon dioxide?

4) What role did the ocean play in the reduction of carbon dioxide?

5) What might have been responsible for the decrease in water vapour?

6) Gases like methane and ammonia were found in the Earth's early atmosphere. Look at the equations below and use them to _explain_ the changes in the composition of the Earth's atmosphere.

> Ammonia + Oxygen → Nitrogen + Water
> $$4NH_{3\,(g)} + 3O_{2(g)} \rightarrow 2N_{2(g)} + 6H_2O_{(g)}$$
> Methane + Oxygen → Carbon dioxide + Water
> $$CH_{4(g)} + 2O_{2(g)} \rightarrow CO_{2(g)} + 2H_2O_{(g)}$$

7) _At this time ultraviolet light radiation from the Sun was intense. This changed diatomic oxygen to triatomic oxygen._

   a) What do the words _"diatomic"_ and _"triatomic"_ mean?

   b) _Give_ another name for _triatomic_ oxygen.

   c) What _useful effect_ does the layer of triatomic oxygen around the Earth have?

8) _Bacteria convert ammonia into nitrates._ How does this help plant growth?

9) _About 350 million years ago animals started to develop. Animals do not require sunlight to make food._ _Which gas_ did they require to be present to survive?

10) _Animals respire._ Write a _word equation_ for respiration.

11) _Carbon that has been locked up for millions of years is returned to the atmosphere when fossil fuels are burnt._ _Write_ an equation for this reaction.

12) _The sea and plants remove carbon dioxide from the atmosphere._
   What will happen if processes that absorb the _additional_ carbon dioxide released into the atmosphere from combustion of fossil fuels are _removed_?

Top Tips: This basically boils down to knowing your atmosphere, and knowing how its composition's affected by things like _respiration_, _photosynthesis_ and _burning_. Make sure you know at least rough percentages for _nitrogen_, _oxygen_, _argon_ and _carbon dioxide_ (these are always for _dry_ air, as the _water vapour's_ pretty variable). And don't forget that if something's being burnt or oxidised, gases might be _released_ — so always think of the _equation_.

The Greenhouse Effect

Most scientists think that the Greenhouse Effect will contribute to global warming. This happens because greenhouse gases, like carbon dioxide and methane, trap infrared radiation inside the atmosphere, which causes it to warm. The higher temperatures could cause the ice caps to melt — raising the sea levels. With more water about, low-lying areas could flood, while other areas of the world could experience severe droughts.

How the Greenhouse Works

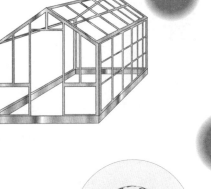

1) _Explain_ using the diagram opposite how a greenhouse keeps plants warm.
2) How is the _radiant energy_ in sunlight kept in the greenhouse?

The Earth as a Greenhouse

3) _Explain_ using the diagram opposite how the atmosphere can act like a _greenhouse_, warming the planet up (the atmosphere is _not_ drawn to scale).

4) What might happen to _global temperatures_ if the greenhouse effect continues to intensify?

5) _Name two_ areas in Britain and two areas in the rest of the world that are low-lying and would be affected if the sea level rose.

6) _The table opposite lists the main contributors to the greenhouse effect._

   a) _Draw_ a pie chart to illustrate these results.
   b) Which gas is the _main contributor_ to this effect?
   c) What are humans doing to _increase_ the levels of this gas in the atmosphere?
   d) _Where_ might you find a CFC?
   e) What does _CFC_ stand for?
   f) What are manufacturers who traditionally used CFCs doing to help _prevent_ global warming and damage to the ozone layer?
   g) Rotting vegetation adds to the greenhouse effect by producing methane. _How else_ might the methane get into the atmosphere?

Gas	% Greenhouse Gas
Methane	14
CFCs	14
Nitrogen	5
Carbon dioxide	57
Surface ozone	10

7) _Look at the table opposite._

   a) What happened in the _early 1800s_ to account for the rise in global temperatures?
   b) _Figures are projected for the years 2050 and 2100._
   What can _we do_ to ensure these figures are not reached?

Year	Approximate global temperature change
1800	0.0
1850	0.1
1900	0.2
1950	0.5
2000	1.0
2050	2.0
2100	4.0

Acid Rain

Rainwater is naturally acidic due to carbon dioxide in the atmosphere. This dissolves in water to make a weakly acidic solution.

> Carbon dioxide + Water → Carbonic acid

However combustion of fossil fuel releases pollutants into the atmosphere like sulphur dioxide and oxides of nitrogen. These also react with water and produce an even more acidic solution.

> Sulphur dioxide + Water → Sulphurous acid
> *(Further oxidation produces sulphuric acid)*

At very high temperatures inside a car engine, nitrogen oxidises to make oxides of nitrogen, often written as NO_x (because many oxides form). These can form nitric acid on reaction with water. The acid rain falls down to Earth, damaging the environment.

Causes and Effects of Acid Rain

1) Why is rain water *naturally acidic*? Which acid does it naturally contain?

2) *Write out* a symbol equation for the reaction of carbon dioxide with water.

3) What is a *fossil fuel*?

4) *Name* three fossil fuels.

5) Give another *name* for combustion.

6) Name *three* pollutant gases which are released on combustion of some fossil fuels?

7) *Name two* acids which are not naturally found in rain water.

8) What effect do you think acid rain might have on a) fish in lakes b) trees in forests?

9) *Most of the sulphur dioxide produced worldwide comes from industry and power stations.*

   a) What do power stations *burn* to produce sulphur dioxide?

   b) What do you feel they should do to *reduce the level* of this gas in the atmosphere?

Reducing Emissions

10) *Power stations now have chemical scrubbers that remove the acid gases in the emissions.* *Give the name* of a type of reaction that will remove the acid gases.

11) Name a *cheap substance* that could be used to remove these gases.

12) *Road traffic is a major producer of oxides of nitrogen.*

   a) What are *all new cars* in Britain required to have to help *reduce the emission* of these gases?

   b) What other very *harmful gas* is found in significant quantities in exhaust fumes?

   c) *Nickel and rhodium can be used to reduce exhaust emission from cars by converting the carbon monoxide to carbon dioxide and the oxides of nitrogen to nitrogen.* Give the *advantages* and *disadvantages* of this.

Top Tips:
These things really bring home how delicate the atmosphere is. There's three parts here — the *greenhouse effect*, *acid rain*, and the *ozone hole* — and being pretty topical, they're likely to be in the Exam. They're all completely *separate* — make sure you understand why. Try drawing a *flow diagram* for each effect — that'll tell you if you really know them. Make sure you know the *causes* and *effects* for each.

The Carbon Cycle

The Importance of Carbon

1) *Carbon is an important and naturally-occurring element found in all living things.*
   Name three nutrients found in plants and animals that contain carbon.

2) *Give one* reason why carbon is such a vital element to all living things.

3) *Glucose is combined with oxygen in the cells to release energy.*
   a) What is the *name* of this process?
   b) *Write* an equation to describe the process.
   c) Why is this process important in the carbon cycle?

Carbon Dioxide Balance

4) How is the balance of carbon dioxide in the atmosphere maintained by plants and animals?

5) What *percentage* of the atmosphere is carbon dioxide?

6) *Photosynthesis is an important process for maintaining the carbon dioxide balance in the atmosphere.* *Write* an equation for this reaction.

7) How can carbon be passed from plants and animals to human beings?

8) *It is possible that carbon in a molecule of carbon dioxide you breathed out has found its way to a protein molecule in the body of a cow.*
   Explain in as much detail as you can how this could happen.

9) CO_2 *is constantly being removed and added to the atmosphere. Which of the processes in the following boxes add carbon dioxide to the atmosphere, and which remove it from the atmosphere?*

| Decay | Photosynthesis | Absorption by oceans |

| Making of carbonate deposits | Respiration | Combustion |

10) How is it possible for carbon compounds that have been *"locked up"* for millions of years underground to be released as CO_2 into the atmosphere? *Name* this process.

Plants and Animals in the Carbon Cycle

11) *Explain* briefly how coal and oil are formed.

12) *Look at the diagram opposite representing part of the carbon cycle.*
   a) *Name* a decomposer in the carbon cycle.
   b) What is the *job* of a decomposer?
   c) How do they *release CO_2* back into the atmosphere?

13) *Fill in* the missing words in the diagram of the carbon cycle.

14) *Animals such as cows and sheep play a major part in the carbon cycle whether alive or dead.* *Explain* why.

15) *Oxygen is important for the continuation of the carbon cycle.* *Explain* in as much detail as you can why this is so.

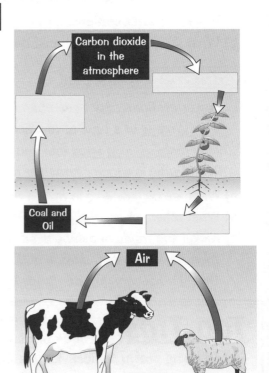

The Carbon Cycle

Carbon and Fossil Fuels

16) How could _carbon_ as CO_2 in the air, over millions of years, become part of a piece of _coal_ deep underground?

The Importance of the Carbon Cycle

17) _Look at the statement made by the scientist:_
Do you agree with the statement? _Explain_ your answer.

"If the carbon cycle ceased — life couldn't continue".

18) _The Sun drives the carbon cycle._ Is this true or false? _Explain_ your reasoning.

19) Why is it so important that carbon can be recycled from one organism to another?

20) _Explain why_ some elements such as carbon, nitrogen, oxygen and hydrogen are described as the "building blocks of life".

21) How could large-scale deforestation effect the carbon cycle worldwide?

22) _An imbalance of carbon dioxide could have a devastating effect on the Earth. Carbon dioxide is being put into the atmosphere as a result of "burning fuels" to produce electricity._

a) Complete the equation for the burning of the fuel methane:

methane + oxygen   →   _____ + _____

b) How could this contribute to the _"greenhouse effect"_?

23) _Complete_ the boxes below with the correct wording (right).

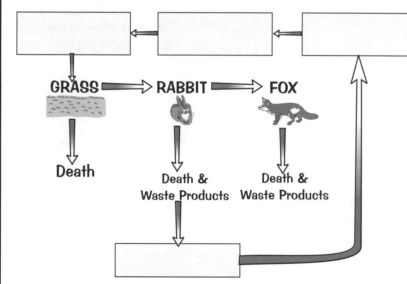

GRASS → RABBIT → FOX

Death

Death &
Waste Products

Death &
Waste Products

Carbon dioxide returned to the atmosphere

Carbon dioxide taken for photosynthesis

Carbon dioxide in the atmosphere

Carbon dioxide released from the remains of living things by decomposers

24) Why are the following important for the carbon cycle?
a) Light.
b) Oxygen.
c) Warmth.

25) Write a _brief summary_ of the carbon cycle, starting with carbon dioxide in the atmosphere.

Top Tips:
It's important stuff, this — life's pretty dependent on _carbon_. But don't forget us humans have a pretty big effect — so don't leave out things like _fossil fuels_. I'd say drawing a _flow diagram_ is the best way to learn cycles like this — as long as you check them afterwards. If you're stuck, try thinking through how each of these fit into the cycle — _land_, _oceans_, _animals_, _plants_, _bacteria_ and _humans_ — it might just jog your memory.

The Nitrogen Cycle

Nitrogen and its Uses

1) What percentage of the atmosphere is nitrogen?

2) *Nitrogen is an important part of proteins.* *Name other* elements that can be found in proteins.

3) How do plants get the *nutrients* they need to make proteins?

4) *Name two* natural processes that put nitrogen into the soil.

5) *The Haber Process is important in maintaining the balance of nitrates in the soil.*
   a) What is made in the Haber Process and what raw materials are used?
   b) Why is it important for maintaining the balance of nitrates in the soil?

6) *Most plants cannot use nitrogen directly from the air as it has to be 'fixed'.*
   What do you understand by the term *"fixed"* in this context?

7) *Some crops are able to use nitrogen directly from the air.*
   a) *Name a crop* that is able to do this.
   b) *Farmers grow these crops at regular intervals on a field.* *Explain* why they do this.

8) Describe *two* routes by which the nitrogen in a plant's proteins can end up in a useful form in the soil.

The Nitrogen Cycle

9) *Fill in* the missing words in the diagram from the list below.

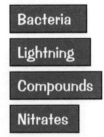

Bacteria

Lightning

Compounds

Nitrates

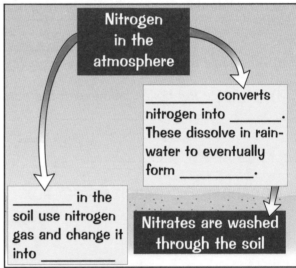

Nitrogen in the atmosphere

_____ converts nitrogen into _____. These dissolve in rain-water to eventually form _____.

_____ in the soil use nitrogen gas and change it into _____

Nitrates are washed through the soil

10) *Name* the type of bacteria found in the root nodules of some plants that convert nitrogen into a form useable by the plant.

11) *Bacteria need energy to convert the nitrogen.* Where does this energy come from?

12) What is the role of nitrifying bacteria in the soil?

13) *Fill in* the missing words from the word list. You may use the words once, more than once or not at all.

Haber	microbes	nitrates	fertilisers	beans	clover
Ammonia	bacteria	nitrogen	nitrifying	nodules
78%	proteins	fixing	atmosphere	photosynthesis	fixed

The _____ contains _____ nitrogen. This nitrogen needs to be _____ so that it can be used. An industrial process known as the _____ Process is important as it converts nitrogen into _____ which is used in making _____. Nitrogen can also be _____ by a certain type of plant such as _____ and _____. These contain _____ _____ in their root _____. Dead plants and animals also put _____ into the soil. They do this because _____ in their bodies are broken down by _____ to ammonium compounds. The nitrates are produced from the ammonium compounds by _____ _____.

The Nitrogen Cycle

Questions on the Nitrogen Cycle

14) What useful function is carried out by _decomposers_ in the soil?

15) Why is it important that microbes in the soil _break down proteins_ from dead organisms?

16) How do humans and other animals _obtain_ the proteins they need?

17) Why are proteins so _essential_ for our bodies?

18) _Nitrates can be very dangerous if they get into rivers._ _Explain_ how this can cause pollution that can lead to the death of fish and other inhabitants.

19) _The demand for manufactured fertilisers has increased over the last years._ _Why_ is this so?

20) _Organic farmers use only natural fertilisers._
    What types of fertiliser could an organic farmer use?

21) How does lightning add _nitrates_ to the soil?

22) Explain how the _nitrogen atoms_ in a molecule of nitrogen (N_2) in the air, could one day finish up as _part of a cell_ in a human body.

23) Why do microbes play such an _essential part_ in the nitrogen cycle?

24) "If microbes were removed from the soil the nitrogen cycle would stop".
    Is this statement true or false? _Explain_ your answer.

Plants and Animals

25) _Look at the diagram opposite._

   a) The blank box represents organisms that convert nitrogen in dead plants and animals to a form useful to plants. Fill in the _name_ of these organisms.

   b) Draw arrows on the diagram to show the _flow of nitrogen_.

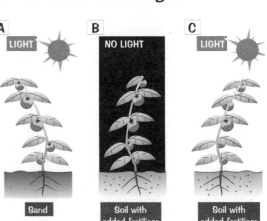

Animal

Plant

Uptake of nitrates by a healthy plant

Death and decay of plants and animals

26) _Plants take up nitrates through their roots to provide themselves with nitrogen._

   a) Apart from making proteins, _why else_ is nitrogen useful to a plant?

   b) How would you notice that a plant _lacked nitrogen_?

27) Why is the recycling of nitrogen _so important_?

28) _Tomato plants were grown in the conditions shown opposite. All the plants had a constant supply of air and water and were kept at $21°C$._

   a) Which plant is likely to produce _the most_ tomatoes? Explain your answer.

   b) Why would the other two produce _less tomatoes_, or none at all?

A — LIGHT — Sand

B — NO LIGHT — Soil with added fertiliser

C — LIGHT — Soil with added fertiliser

Top Tips:
This is probably the toughest of the cycles — too many confusing names, I'd say. Try actually going through it in your mind's eye, _picturing_ all the processes — that'll make remembering it easier. And always start by looking at the _overall form_ of a flow diagram, like where all the _boxes_ and _arrows_ go — then you're less likely to forget the details. Oh yes, and make sure there's no _dead ends_ — otherwise it's not a _cycle_.

The Rock Cycle

The Rock Cycle

1) *Look at* the diagram of the rock cycle opposite.

a) *Fill in* the boxes with words from the list below:

- Transportation
- Metamorphic rocks
- Deposition
- Melting
- Weathering
- Burial and compression
- Igneous rocks

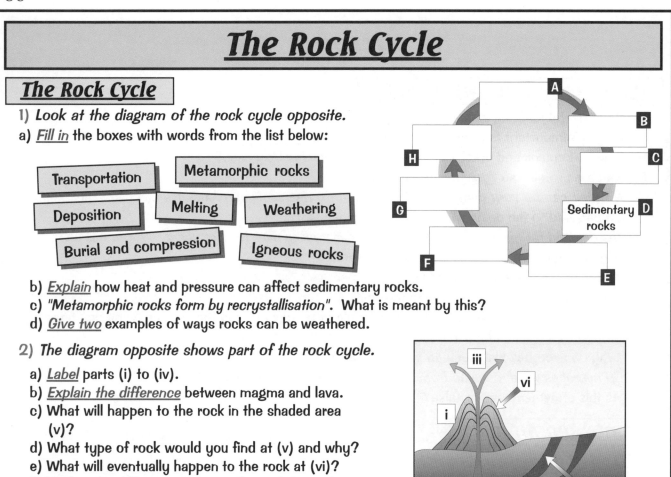

b) *Explain* how heat and pressure can affect sedimentary rocks.

c) *"Metamorphic rocks form by recrystallisation"*. What is meant by this?

d) *Give two* examples of ways rocks can be weathered.

2) *The diagram opposite shows part of the rock cycle.*

a) *Label* parts (i) to (iv).

b) *Explain the difference* between magma and lava.

c) What will happen to the rock in the shaded area (v)?

d) What type of rock would you find at (v) and why?

e) What will eventually happen to the rock at (vi)?

f) *Explain the difference* between the rock formed at (i) and at (iv) on the diagram.

Words and Meanings

3) *Fill in* the table below to explain the following words and how they relate to the rock cycle.

Description	Meaning	Associated with forming:
a) Deposition		Sedimentary rock
b) Burial		Sedimentary and metamorphic rock
c) Melting		
d) Compression		
e) Recrystallisation		

4) *Complete* the following paragraphs by filling in the missing words from the list:

> buried   igneous   metamorphic   weathered   buried   compressed   heat
> melted   magma   sedimentary   millions   sedimentary   metamorphic   magma
> sea   pressure   magma   volcano   erupts   rock cycle

Over _____ of years rocks change from one form to another. This is called the _____. The three main rock types are _____, _____ and igneous. Rock particles get washed into the _____ because they are _____ and transported. Over millions of years these become _____ and _____, and form _____ rock. Sometimes these rocks become _____ deeper into the Earth, and are changed by _____ and _____ into _____ rocks. Metamorphic rock can be buried still further where, completely _____, it becomes _____. Pressure forces the _____ upwards where it either _____ as a _____ or goes into existing cracks in rock and forms _____ rock.

The Rock Cycle

Sedimentary and Metamorphic Rocks

5) What does _metamorphic_ mean?

6) What is the general _term_ given to:
   a) igneous rock that forms _outside_ the crust (from volcanoes).
   b) igneous rock that cools in cracks _in existing rock_.

7) _Fill in_ the table by _naming_ the metamorphic rocks formed from the sedimentary rocks.

Sedimentary rock	Metamorphic rock
a) Limestone	
b) Mudstone	
c) Sandstone	

Rock Types and Properties

8) _Sedimentary and metamorphic rocks are formed deep underground._ Explain how it is possible to see these rocks on the Earth's _surface_.

9) Considering how each type of rock is formed, _explain_ why igneous rock is more resistant to weathering than sedimentary rock.

10) _Give two differences_ between metamorphic and igneous rocks.

11) What name is given to the particles that weather and settle in the sea?

12) _The diagram below shows an outline of the rock cycle._

a) _Label_ all the areas where you would expect to find:

   i) metamorphic rocks.   ii) sedimentary rocks.   iii) igneous rocks.

b) Put the _following labels_ onto the diagram:

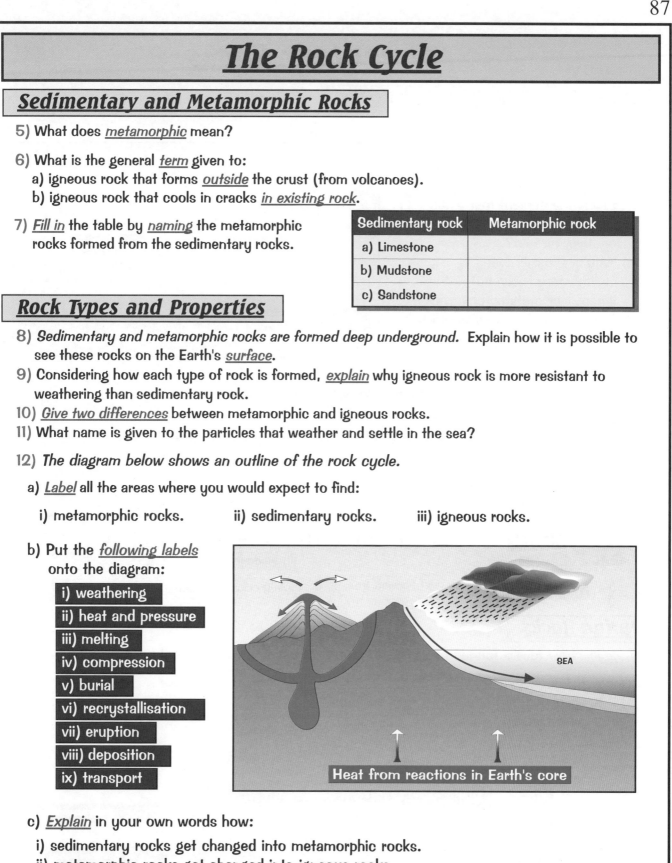

   i) weathering
   ii) heat and pressure
   iii) melting
   iv) compression
   v) burial
   vi) recrystallisation
   vii) eruption
   viii) deposition
   ix) transport

SEA

Heat from reactions in Earth's core

c) _Explain_ in your own words how:

   i) sedimentary rocks get changed into metamorphic rocks.
   ii) metamorphic rocks get changed into igneous rocks.
   iii) igneous and metamorphic rocks get changed into sedimentary rocks.

Top Tips:

Another cycle to learn. But since there's only _three_ basic _rock types_, it really isn't so bad. Draw them in a _triangle_, then think how each can be converted into the other two — and fill in the arrows. There's only _six combinations_, so you'll know if you've missed anything. Just make sure you can _name_ all the processes — and know the _conditions_ they need.

Sedimentary Rocks

Formation of Sedimentary Rocks

1) *The diagram shows the formation of sedimentary rocks.*

a) *Explain* what happens when pressure is applied to a layer of sedimentary rock.

b) How is the cement that holds pieces of sedimentary rock together formed?

c) Why are fossils found in sedimentary rocks but not in igneous or metamorphic rock?

d) Draw *arrows* on the diagram to show which way the following act:

i) transport ii) pressure

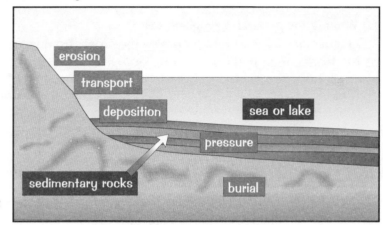

e) *Plant and animal remains decay in sedimentary rock to make a useful substance. Name this useful substance.*

2) *Sedimentary rocks are fragments of other rocks in a natural cement.*
   Explain why the rocks that they are made from can still be identified.

3) *Match* the rocks with the correct descriptions below:

a) Limestone

b) Shale

c) Conglomerate

d) Sandstone

i) Formed from fine particles grey in colour. Will easily split into layers.

ii) Pebbles and chips of rock in a cement.

iii) Made from sand. Particles stuck together.

iv) Formed from shells, mostly calcium carbonate, grey/white colour.

Dating Rocks

4) *Explain* how fossils found in sedimentary rock are used to date the rocks.

5) *Look at the diagram below.*

a) i) In which layer(s) could *limestone* be found?
   ii) In which layer(s) could *marble* be found?

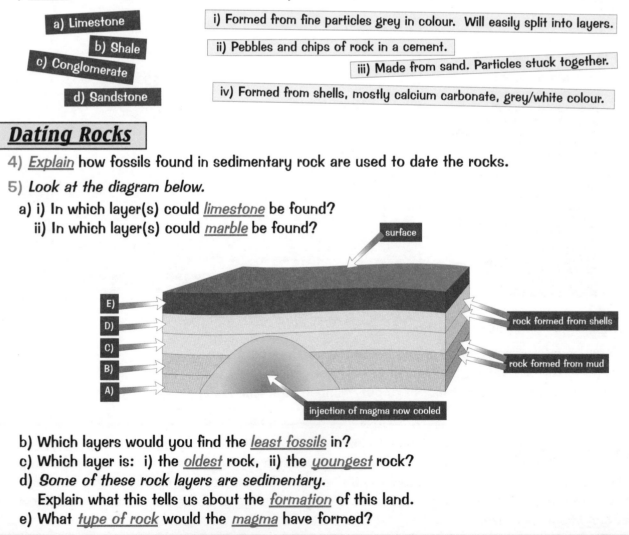

b) Which layers would you find the *least fossils* in?

c) Which layer is: i) the *oldest* rock, ii) the *youngest* rock?

d) *Some of these rock layers are sedimentary.*
   Explain what this tells us about the *formation* of this land.

e) What *type of rock* would the *magma* have formed?

Sedimentary Rocks

Earth Movements

6) *Earth movements cause layers of sedimentary rock to move. An example is shown in the diagram below:*

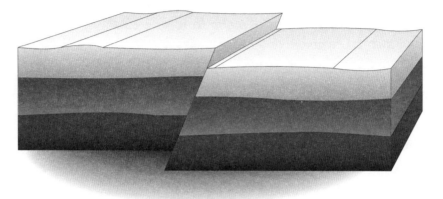

a) How can you tell that the Earth's crust has _moved_?
b) What is this formation _called_?
c) *Although it can be seen that these rocks have moved, it is dating the sedimentary rocks that tells us they are the same age. _Explain_ how sedimentary rocks can be dated.*

Rock Fragments

7) *Look at the diagrams below of different rock fragments.*

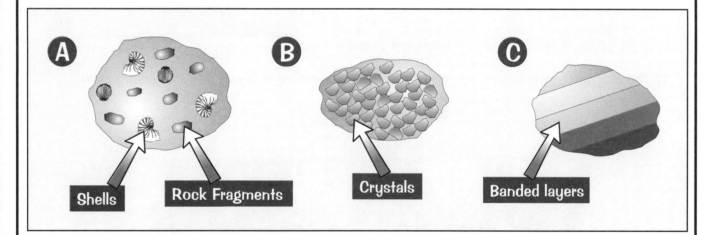

a) For each of A, B and C, state whether it is an igneous, a sedimentary or a metamorphic rock. _Give a reason_ for your choice in each case.
b) _Name_ a possible example of each type of rock.

8) *Granite is much harder than limestone. _Explain why_.*

> **Top Tips:** Pretty straightforward really, these sedimentary rocks — just loads of _particles_ stuck in a _cement_. But you'd better know _what_ the cement is — and _where_ it comes from. The Exams might ask you to identify a sedimentary rock from a picture, so you'd better know a few. Make sure you at least know the differences between _sandstone_, _limestone_, _mudstone_ (_shale_) and _conglomerates_.

Igneous Rocks

Crystal Sizes

1) The size of an igneous rock's <u>crystals</u> depends on the rock's <u>rate of cooling</u> when it was being formed. It is possible to set up an experiment in the lab using <u>SALOL</u> to investigate the relationship between crystal size and rate of cooling. The apparatus is shown opposite. The salol melts to form a clear liquid, which can then be removed and recrystallised.

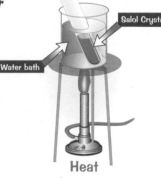

a) Why is it better to use a water bath than to directly heat the crystals over a Bunsen burner?

b) *Explain* a method you could use to ensure that
   (i) the salol cooled quickly
   (ii) the salol cooled slowly

c) Which would give the larger crystals?

2) In some igneous rocks the crystals are visible and in some they are not.

   Explain the following: a) why some igneous rocks have <u>small crystals</u>
   b) why some igneous rocks have <u>large crystals</u>

Formation of Igneous Rocks

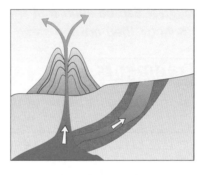

3) *Label* the diagram on the right.
   a) Indicate where you would find:
      i) *Extrusive* igneous rock.
      ii) *Intrusive* igneous rock.
      iii) *Magma*.
      iv) *Lava*.
   b) *Name one* intrusive and one extrusive igneous rock.

4) The diagram below shows a piece of igneous rock amongst layers of sedimentary rock.

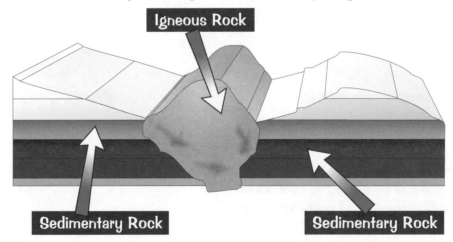

a) How do you think this igneous rock came to be here?

b) *Explain* why in a few thousand years this lump of igneous rock may stand well above the rest of the landscape.

5) Sometimes igneous rock, such as pumice, can be very light and have holes in it.
   Explain how pumice is formed and why it has this form.

Metamorphic Rocks

Formation of Metamorphic Rocks

1) What causes rocks underground to be subjected to large forces?

2) *The diagram below shows a section of the rock cycle where metamorphic rocks form.*

   a) <u>Write</u> on the diagram:
     i) where <u>pressure</u> acts.
     ii) where <u>heat</u> comes from.

   b) Why do metamorphic rocks <u>recrystallise</u>?
   c) Where in the diagram might <u>magma</u> be formed?
   d) Where does the <u>heat</u> come from to cause rock changes?

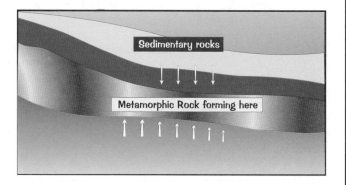

Types of Metamorphic Rocks

3) <u>Identify</u> the following metamorphic rocks from their descriptions:

   a) | Small sugary crystals, white/grey in colour |

   b) | Grey, can be split into layers |

   c) | Layers of crystals, including dark mica |

4) *Slate and schist are both formed from mudstone and shale.* What causes the <u>difference</u> between them?

5) *People grow crops near volcanic areas even though there are risks of volcanic eruptions.* Explain why the soil there is <u>so fertile</u>?

6) *Look at the table below.*

   a) <u>Complete</u> the table by giving uses for the various types of rock.

Rock	Use
Sandstone	
Limestone	
Slate	
Marble	

   b) Why are metamorphic rocks generally <u>harder</u> and more <u>resistant to erosion</u> than sedimentary rocks?

Top Tips: There's not that many things they can ask you here. Exam favourites include how <u>crystal sizes</u> of igneous rocks depend on the <u>rate of cooling</u>, and how particular metamorphic rocks have formed. So you'd better know your <u>slate</u> from your <u>marble</u> and <u>schist</u> — and be able to say say <u>what</u> they're formed from, and under what <u>conditions</u>. And just make sure you can tell your <u>intrusive</u> from your <u>extrusive</u> igneous rocks.

A Summary of Rock Types

Rock Types and Properties

1) *Match* the correct rock to the type:

Marble   Sandstone

Shale   Schist

Slate   Granite

Igneous

Sedimentary

Metamorphic

2) *Complete* the following sentences using the correct words from the list below:

| metamorphic | crystallise | large | cement | fossils | melted | basalt |
| water | granite | pressure | cements | melt | sedimentary | magma |

_____ is an example of an intrusive igneous rock. It has _____ crystals. _____ is an example of an extrusive igneous rock. Sedimentary rocks contain _____ which will not be present in igneous or metamorphic rocks because they would have _____ or changed. Sedimentary rocks contain a natural _____ which is made because _____ squeezes the _____ out and salts _____, which _____ particles together. Metamorphic rocks are formed when _____ rocks are heated and compressed. The sedimentary rock does not _____ or _____ would be formed and not _____ rock.

3) *Complete* the following sentences using the correct words from the list below:

| volcano | intrusive | magma | small | large | extrusive | erupts |

a) _____ igneous rocks cool slowly and have _____ crystals. _____ goes into existing cracks in rock.

b) _____ igneous rocks cool quickly and have _____ crystals. Magma _____ from the inside of the earth in a _____.

4) *Complete* the following sentences using the correct words from the list below:

| heat | sedimentary | heated | melt | texture | injection | metamorphic | Earth | pressure |

_____ rocks are changed into _____ rock by _____ and _____. _____ movements push rocks underground. The _____ of metamorphic rocks is changed but the rocks do not _____. If they did, they would not be metamorphic rocks. Metamorphic rocks can also form when an _____ of magma in cracks in existing rocks causes the rock around to be _____.

SECTION FIVE — AIR AND ROCK

An Earth Science Crossword

Fill in the Crossword using the Clues below:

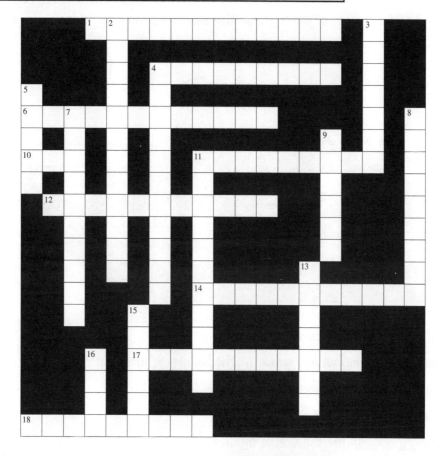

Across

1) Most dense type of tectonic plate (7,5)
4) Igneous rocks that form on the surface of the Earth (9)
6) Scale used to measure earthquake intensity (6,5)
10) Energy source which drives the rock cycle on the surface of the Earth (3)
11) Often seen when two continental plates collide (9)
12) Type of plate margin where one plate dips beneath the other (11)
14) Type of decay that creates the Earth's heat (11)
17) Rock containing layers of fine particles (11)
18) Common carbonate rock (9)

Down

2) Type of plate margin where new rocks are formed (12)
3) Rock type formed from molten magma (7)
4) Often experienced on the San Andreas Fault (11)
5) Layer of the Earth about 35km thick (5)
7) Currents which cause plate movement (9)
8) Igneous rocks that form inside the Earth (10)
9) State of the outer core (6)
11) Rocks formed by the action of heat and pressure on sedimentary rocks (11)
13) All the continents were originally joined up to make this (7)
15) Example of an igneous rock (6)
16) Centre of the Earth (4)

Top Tips: You'd better know your rocks. The Exam might ask for _examples_ of each type — but failing that you'll probably have to name a rock type from a _picture_ or a description of how it's _formed_. So make sure you know which _features_ go with each type. Check you know these for a start — _cement_, _fossils_, _crystals_, _hardness_ and _layers_.

The Water Cycle

A Natural Recycling Process

1) **The water cycle has four distinct parts.** Use the words in the box to label the diagram:

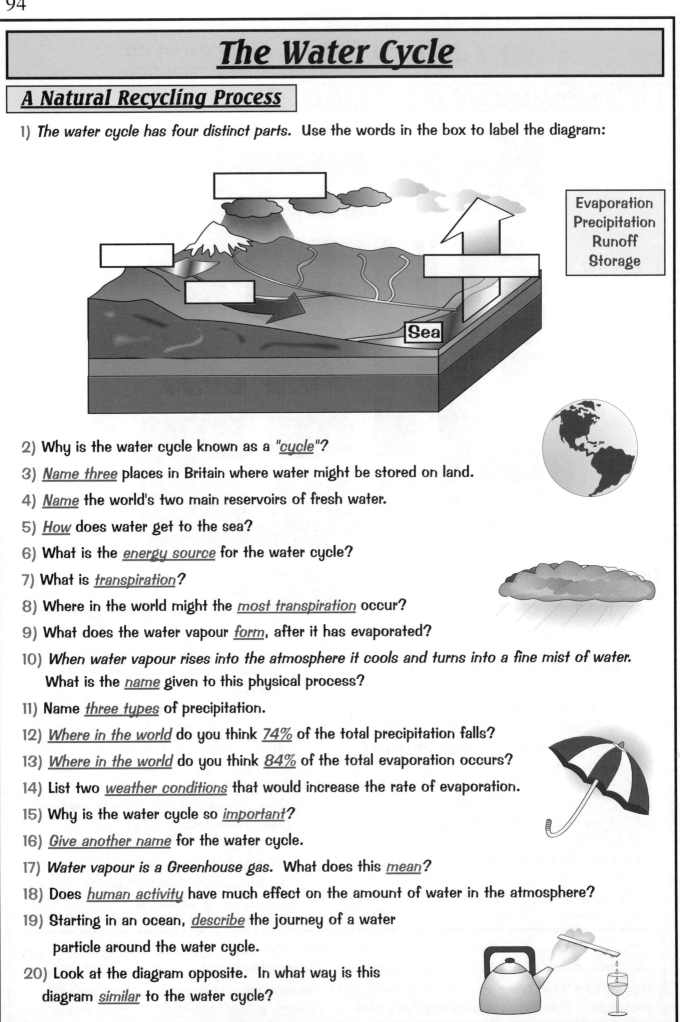

Evaporation
Precipitation
Runoff
Storage

Sea

2) Why is the water cycle known as a _"cycle"_?

3) _Name three_ places in Britain where water might be stored on land.

4) _Name_ the world's two main reservoirs of fresh water.

5) _How_ does water get to the sea?

6) What is the _energy source_ for the water cycle?

7) What is _transpiration_?

8) Where in the world might the _most transpiration_ occur?

9) What does the water vapour _form_, after it has evaporated?

10) **When water vapour rises into the atmosphere it cools and turns into a fine mist of water.** What is the _name_ given to this physical process?

11) Name _three types_ of precipitation.

12) _Where in the world_ do you think _74%_ of the total precipitation falls?

13) _Where in the world_ do you think _84%_ of the total evaporation occurs?

14) List two _weather conditions_ that would increase the rate of evaporation.

15) Why is the water cycle so _important_?

16) _Give another name_ for the water cycle.

17) **Water vapour is a Greenhouse gas.** What does this _mean_?

18) Does _human activity_ have much effect on the amount of water in the atmosphere?

19) **Starting in an ocean, _describe_ the journey of a water particle around the water cycle.**

20) Look at the diagram opposite. In what way is this diagram _similar_ to the water cycle?

Weathering and Erosion

The Three Types of Weathering

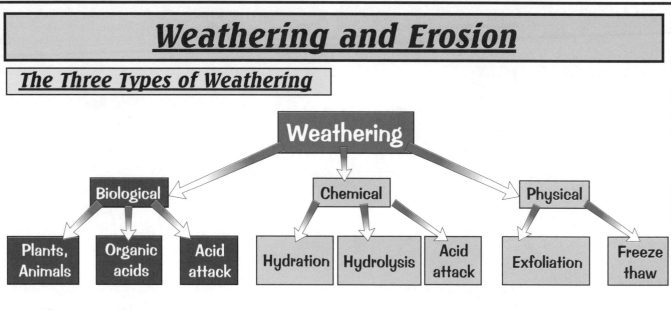

1) What is _weathering_?
2) _Name the three_ main types of weathering.
3) _Give one_ example of how a plant might weather a rock.
4) _Give one_ example of how an animal might weather a rock.
5) _Exfoliation is often called onion skin weathering._ _Explain_ what this means.
6) How does _exfoliation_ work?
7) _Organic acids like humic acid may form in some soils._ _Name_ a rock that might be weathered, and so weakened, by this acid.
8) _Carbon dioxide in the air makes rain water naturally acidic, so when it falls on carbonate rocks it can cause a reaction._ How do humans _add_ to this type of weathering?

9) A student placed a glass sample tube full of water in a freezer over night. In the morning the tube was cracked.

   a) Why did the tube crack?
   b) How can the results help us to _explain_ freeze-thaw weathering?

Before **After**

Rocks and Weathering

10) Which of the three main rock types is generally the easiest to weather?
11) _When rocks have been weathered they often form fine sediment that is transported by wind or water._ _Name three_ ways in which water might carry off sediment.
12) What is _erosion_ and which processes does it include?
13) _Sedimentary rocks are formed from the sediment that is made by erosion._ What other vitally important substance is made from this process?

Top Tips:
Weathering's basically just the breaking up of rocks by _acid_ or _things getting inside_ them. If the _surface_ is wearing away and it's not down to acid, then _erosion's_ a pretty safe bet. Once you understand that, it's just a case of knowing the different _types_ of weathering — together with a few examples. The _water cycle's_ not too complicated, but still make sure you can draw a _flow diagram_ — then you'll know you know it.

The Earth's Structure

Layers of the Earth

1) Approximately _what proportion_ of the Earth's surface is water?
2) Why is the Earth known as the _blue_ planet?
3) _Name_ the main layers within the Earth.
4) _Complete_ the diagram below by labelling the layers you named in question 3.

5) _Link up_ the part of the Earth with the correct description:

Mantle	2,225 km	solid	iron and nickel
Inner core	20-35Km	dense liquid	iron / magnesium silicates
Outer core	2,900 km	rock that can flow due to high forces	iron and nickel
Crust	1,275 km	solid rock	oxygen, silicon, aluminium

Inside the Earth

6) _The temperature rises as you go deeper into the Earth. This is because heat is produced inside the Earth by radioactive isotopes._

   a) What is an _isotope_?
   b) What does the term _radioactive_ mean?
   c) Why does the Earth _not cool down_ from radiation, like a kettle of hot water would?
   d) _This heating causes convection currents to form._ What do these _convection currents_ cause?

7) _Name_ the two types of crust.
8) Why does the crust _float_ and not _sink_ into the mantle below it?
9) _The crust is divided into about a dozen continental plates._ _Give another name_ for continental plates.

The Earth's Structure

Earthquakes

When a major earthquake occurs, shock waves and echoes are felt all over the world. Scientists use these _seismic waves_ to find out about the structure of the Earth. There are two types of seismic waves — P (primary) waves and S (secondary) waves.

1) Why do _earthquakes_ occur?

2) _Complete_ the table of the properties of P and S seismic waves, using the words given in the boxes:

| slow | transverse | longitudinal |

| solids and liquids | | just solids | fast | when the density of the material alters |

	P waves	S waves
Speed		
Wave type		
Will travel through		
Refracted		

3) Look at the diagram below, which shows where P and S waves might be detected.

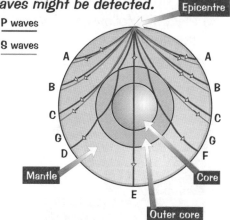

P waves
S waves

Epicentre

Mantle

Core

Outer core

a) What is the _epicentre_ of an earthquake?

b) P and S waves can be detected at points A B and C. What does this tell us about the _state_ of the mantle?

c) Only P waves can be detected at points D and F. What does that tell you about _state_ of the outer core?

d) Why are _no S waves_ detected at point G?

e) Why are _no P waves_ detected at point G?

Elements in the Earth's Crust

4) Look at the table showing the abundance of various elements in the Earth's crust.

Element	% by mass in Earth's crust
Oxygen	50
Silicon	26
Aluminium	7
Iron	4
Calcium	3
Potassium	2.5
Sodium	2.5
Magnesium	2
Hydrogen	1
Other	2

a) Put this information into a _pie chart_.

b) Which is the _most abundant_ metal?

c) Which is the _most abundant_ non-metal?

d) Are all these elements found as _pure elements_ in the Earth's crust?

e) Aluminium costs about _three times_ as much as iron to buy. Why do you think this is?

Top Tips: The Earth's structure really isn't too involved — it's just a case of knowing the _composition_ of the four parts, and which _one_ is liquid. Remember that most of the mantle's _solid_ — even though it slowly flows under the enormous _temperatures_ and _pressures_. The other main thing to know is the _evidence_ for this structure — make sure you know what _seismic waves_, _magnetism_ and _meteorites_ tell us.

Plate Tectonics and Plate Boundaries

Plate Movement

1) The map shows the two continents South America and Africa. The line between them shows where a plate boundary occurs.

a) On the diagram _draw arrows_ to show which way the continents are moving.

b) What causes the movement?

c) _Give three_ pieces of evidence that would show these continents were once part of the same landmass.

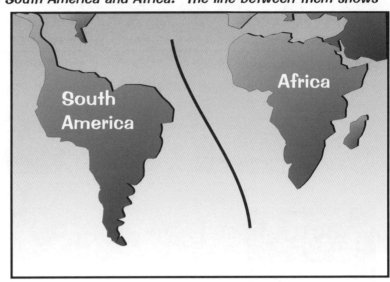

Diagram of Plate Movement

2) Look at the diagram below showing plate movement and its effects.

a) Place the following _labels_ on the diagram:

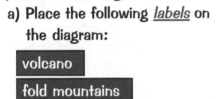

volcano

fold mountains

zone of earthquakes

continental plate

oceanic plate

regions where magma may be found

subduction zone

b) _Draw arrows_ to show any movement of the plates.

c) Why are volcanoes formed when this type of collision occurs?

d) _Fill in_ the missing words to describe what is happening, using this list:

continental	volcanoes	zone	affect	oceanic	continental
	pressure	earthquakes	kilometres	movement	

The _____ plate is forced under the _____ plate. The oceanic crust melts due to heat; this causes a build up of _____, and molten rock forces its way to the surface in _____. A _____ of _____ occurs as the oceanic crust sinks beneath the _____ crust. This type of Earth _____ can _____ areas many _____ away.

e) What is the name given to this type of plate boundary?

Plate Tectonics and Plate Boundaries

The Mid-Atlantic Ridge

3) A plate boundary can be constructive and make new ground — like the mid-Atlantic ridge
running through the Atlantic Ocean.

a) Draw _arrows_ on the diagram to
show the movement of the
plates:

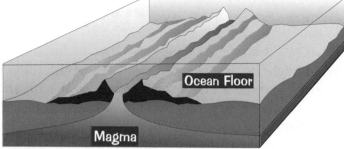

b) Why does magma _rise_?

c) What _rock_ type does this magma
produce?

d) The plate boundary running along the middle of the Atlantic Ocean has ridges on either side.
How does this provide _evidence_ for continental drift?

e) The magnetic orientation of the rocks also provides strong evidence for continental drift.
Explain what this is, and why it provides _evidence_ for continental drift.

Collision of Continental Plates

4) Sometimes two continental plates collide.

a) _Explain_ with the help of a diagram what happens when two continental plates collide.

b) _Name an area_ of the world relatively recently formed as a result of this type of collision.

5) San Francisco is sitting on a famous fault line.

a) What is the _name_ of this fault line?

b) _Explain_ what is happening on San Francisco's fault line.

6) These movements of crust are due to lots of activity in the core and mantle. Radioactive
decay in the core produces heat which sets up convection currents in the mantle.
Describe with the help of a diagram what you understand by _convection currents_.

7) _Fill in_ the missing words in the sentences below, using this list:

| polarity | ocean | South America | Africa | floor | spreading | rock strata |
| half-a-million | mid-Atlantic ridge | | plate tectonics | | land mass | jigsaw |

There is now much evidence for _____. Many pieces of land
fit together like a _____ puzzle and it is thought they were all once part of the
same _____. Identical plants and animal fossils have been found
on either side of the oceans in _____ and _____. A
strong piece of evidence is also that of _____. They show a marked
age similarity in both continents. The Earth's magnetic field swaps _____
roughly every _____ years. In the _____ floor by the
_____ _____, the magnetic 'bands' either side of the ridge are the
same. This suggests that the sea _____ is _____.

Top Tips: There's basically _four_ types of boundary — it just depends on the types
of plates and whether they're _colliding_, _moving apart_, or _scraping_ by each
other. Make sure you can give an _example_ of each type, and know what happens there. The
other stuff you need to know is the _evidence_ for plate tectonics — just make sure you know
what _fossils_, _living creatures_, _rocks_, _magnetic stripes_, and the _shapes of the continents_ tell us.

The Periodic Table

Facts about the Periodic Table

1) In the Periodic table what is meant by a *Group*?
2) In the Periodic table what is meant by a *Period*?
3) Roughly *how many* elements are there?
4) In what *order* are the elements listed?
5) What might be *similar* about members of the same group?
6) What might be *similar* about members of the same period?
7) Whose *idea* was it to put the elements in this order?
8) If an element is in Group I then *how many* electrons will it have in its outer electron shell?
9) If an ion has a 2+ charge, then *which group* is it most likely to be in?
10) If an ion has a 1- charge, then *which group* is it most likely to be in?

Some Elements in the Periodic Table

11) In this Periodic Table, some elements are shown as letters:

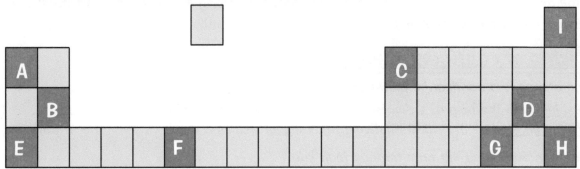

These letters are **NOT** the proper symbols for the elements.

Choose *one* letter from the above Periodic Table to answer each of the following questions:

WHICH ELEMENT(S).........

(a) are Noble gases?
(b) are Halogens?
(c) is in Group II?
(d) is in the same period as D?
(e) has three electrons in its outer shell?
(f) has an atomic number of 3?
(g) are non-metals?
(h) is a transition element?
(i) would form an ION with a charge of 1^+?
(j) will not form an ion easily?
(k) would form an ion by gaining 2 electrons per atom?
(l) would form an ion with as many electrons as an atom of element (I)?
(m) are the least reactive of those marked in the table?

12) *Complete* this table by filling in the *electronic configurations* of the elements:

Period	Group 1	Group 2	Group 3	Group 7	Group 0
2	Li 2,1	Be	B	F	Ne
3	Na	Mg	Al	Cl	Ar 2,8,8

The Periodic Table

Group I of the Periodic Table

13) Select the correct *highlighted* words to describe Group I:

a) All the elements are *metals / non-metals*.
b) They are all *hard / soft* substances with a *high / low* density.
c) They are all very *reactive / unreactive* and are kept in a bottle of *oil / water*.
d) They tarnish *easily / with difficulty* in air.
e) They become *more / less* reactive going down the Group.
f) A typical member of the group is *calcium / sodium*.
g) They form 1^+ / 1^- ions.

Group VII of the Periodic Table

14) Select the correct *highlighted* words to describe Group VII:

a) All the elements are *metallic / non-metallic*.
b) They are mostly *conductors / non-conductors* of electricity.
c) Going down the Group their melting points *increase / decrease*.
d) Chlorine is a *solid / liquid / gas* at RTP.
e) Bromine is a *solid / liquid / gas* at RTP.
f) Iodine is a *solid / liquid / gas* at RTP.
g) Down the Group they get *lighter / darker* in colour.
h) They form 1^+ / 1^- ions.

More Questions about the Periodic Table

15) Many Periodic Tables have a *zig-zag* line on them. What does this line *divide*?
16) *Where* are the *metals* in the Periodic Table in relation to this line?
17) *Where* are the *non-metals* in the Periodic Table in relation to this line?
18) Some elements are known as *semi-metals* or *metalloids*.
    a) *Where* are these elements found in the Periodic Table?
    b) Give *one example* of a *semi-metal* element.
19) One element is *unlike* any other as it is *not* a member of any group. *Name* this element.
20) Where are the *transition metals* found on the Periodic Table?
21) *Members of Group III form 3+ ions.* What ions do members of *Group II* form?
22) What is the *charge* on an ion made from an element in *Group VI*?
23) Which is the *most reactive* member of Group I?
24) Which is the *most reactive* member of Group II?
25) *Sodium has an atomic number of 11 and a mass number of 23.*
   Explain in as much detail as possible what this tells us about an atom of sodium.

Top Tips: The *Periodic Table's* actually pretty handy — you can get a good idea of the *properties* of an element just by where it is. Remember that groups *"group"* things with similar properties, whereas periods show *"periodic variation"* as you cross them — that way you won't forget which is which. You must know how *size* and *reactivity* vary around the table — and make sure you can find your *metals*, *non-metals*, and *noble gases*.

Group 0 — The Noble Gases

General Properties of the Noble Gases

1) Why are the Noble gases sometimes known as *Group VIII*?
2) *The Noble gases are "inert". What does this mean?*
3) By referring to their atomic structure, *explain why* the Noble gases are "inert".
4) Use the table to *answer* these questions:

a) Why would you expect hydrogen and helium to be *gases* at room temperature and pressure?

b) For a given number of atoms, which of helium and hydrogen is the *heaviest*?

	Hydrogen	Helium
Structure of Atom		
Boiling Point °C	-253	-269
Melting Point °C	-259	-272
Atomic Number	1	2
Mass Number	2	4

c) *Write down* the number of protons, electrons and neutrons in an atom of hydrogen and an atom of helium.

d) *Explain why* a sample of helium is more dense than a sample of hydrogen under the same conditions.

e) *If chlorine gas was burnt in hydrogen, a reaction would occur forming hydrogen chloride. What do you think would happen if chlorine was burnt in helium? Explain your answer.*

5) Why is *helium* used in airships rather than hydrogen?

6) *Hydrogen atoms are diatomic and helium atoms monatomic.*

a) What is meant by *"diatomic"* and *"monatomic"*?

b) Why do some elements form monatomic molecules and others form diatomic molecules?

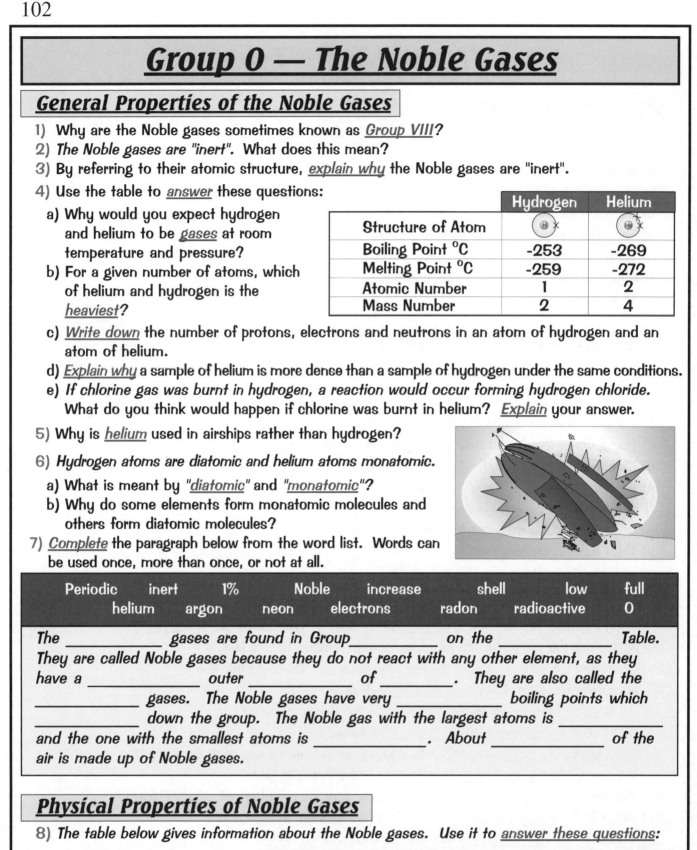

7) *Complete* the paragraph below from the word list. Words can be used once, more than once, or not at all.

Periodic	inert	1%	Noble	increase	shell	low	full
helium	argon	neon	electrons	radon	radioactive	0	

The _____ gases are found in Group_____ on the _____ Table. They are called Noble gases because they do not react with any other element, as they have a _____ outer _____ of _____. They are also called the _____ gases. The Noble gases have very _____ boiling points which _____ down the group. The Noble gas with the largest atoms is _____ and the one with the smallest atoms is _____. About _____ of the air is made up of Noble gases.

Physical Properties of Noble Gases

8) *The table below gives information about the Noble gases. Use it to* answer these questions:

a) How do the *melting and boiling points* of the gases change as you go down the group?

b) *Complete* the table by estimating the melting point and boiling point of radon.

Noble Gas	Atomic Number	Density at STP g/cm³	Melting Point °C	Boiling Point °C
Helium	2	0.00017	-272	-269
Neon	10	0.00084	-248	-246
Argon	18	0.0016	-189	-186
Krypton	36	0.0034	-157	-153
Xenon	54	0.006	-112	-107
Radon	86	0.01		

c) Why do the *densities* of the Noble gases increase down the group?

Group 0 — The Noble Gases

Discovery and Uses of the Noble Gases

Element	When discovered
Iron	Ancient times
Helium	1895
Neon	1898
Oxygen	1774
Phosphorus	1669

9) *Look* at the table opposite.
   a) Why do you think the Noble gases proved harder to *discover* than other elements?
   b) *The percentages of noble gases in the air are as follows:*
      Ar 0.93%, Ne 0.0018%, He 0.0005%,
         Kr 0.0001%, Xe 0.0001%.
   Approximately what percentage of air do noble gases make up?
   c) Why may it have been *easier* to discover argon than the other Noble gases?

10) *Answer* these questions about neon.
    a) Why is neon used in *advertising signs*?   b) Give another *use* of neon.

11) Give a *common use* for argon and state why it is used for that purpose.

12) What *process* could be used to obtain a sample of argon?

13) *Radon-222 is an inert gas, but is radioactive.*
    What is meant by *"radioactive"*?

14) *Some Noble gases are used in lasers.* What are *lasers* used for?

15) Why is helium used in *meteorological balloons*, rather than argon?

Neon is Ace!

Questions on Electronic Configuration

16) *The table below shows some details of the Noble gases.*
    a) *Fill in the gaps* in the table.
    b) *Write down* an element of Group 0 to match each of these descriptions:
       i) Gives out a light when a current is passed through it.
       ii) Less dense than air.
       iii) Used in lasers.

Noble Gas	Symbol	Atomic Number	Mass Number	No. of Protons	No. of Electrons	No. of Neutrons
	He		4	2		
Neon			20	10		
	Ar	18	40			
Krypton			84	36		
Xenon		54	131		54	
Radon		86	222			

17) *Draw* an atom each of Neon ($^{20}_{10}$Ne) and Argon ($^{40}_{18}$Ar), showing their electronic configurations.

18) *Why* would you expect all the elements in Group 0 to have similar properties?

19) *When lithium becomes a lithium ion, Li^+, it has the same number of electrons as helium.*
    a) *Draw* a lithium ion Li^+ and a helium atom, $^4_2$He.
    b) *Label* on each atom the number of protons, neutrons and electrons.
    c) *Although they now have the same electronic configuration, they are not the same atom.* Why is this?

20) When a potassium atom becomes a potassium ion (K^+), it has the same electronic configuration as *which* Noble gas?

21) Which Noble gases have the same electronic configuration as the following?

    a) Oxide ion, O^{2-} b) Sodium ion, Na^+ c) Chloride ion, Cl^-

22) If at standard atmospheric pressure argon has a melting point of –189 °C and a boiling point of –186 °C, over what temperature ranges would it be a *liquid* and a *gas*?

Top Tips: The thing about noble gases is they *don't do anything*. But you'd better know *why* they don't do anything — as the examiners like to ask. And don't forget they're all *single-atom* gases. Other than that, just make sure you know their uses — check you know which are used in *balloons*, *discharge tubes*, *bulbs* and *lasers*.

Group 1 — The Alkali Metals

Basic Facts about the Alkali Metals

1) Group 1 of the Periodic Table is known as the _Alkali Metals_.

   a) Why is Group 1 of the Periodic Table known as the _Alkali Metals_?

   b) Why are they known as "_Group 1_" in the Periodic Table?

2) How are the Alkali metals _stored_ and why are they stored this way?

3) Alkali metals react with water to produce a gas and a solution.

   a) What _colour_ would the resulting solution be if universal indicator was added?

   b) What would be the _pH_ of the resulting solution?

4) The table on the right shows four alkali metals and some of their physical properties.

Alkali Metal	Atomic Mass	Symbol	Boiling Point °C	Melting Point °C	Density g/cm³
Lithium	7		1342	181	0.535
Sodium	23		880	98	0.971
Potassium	39		760	63	0.862
Rubidium	85.5		688	39	1.53

   a) Complete the table by filling in their _symbols_.

   b) Caesium is the next alkali metal. Estimate its:

     i) _Boiling point_   ii) _Melting point_   iii) _Density_.

   c) _Explain_ why, as you go down Group 1, the atoms get _bigger_ in cross-section.

   d) Which member of the group is the _most dense_, and why?

   e) What must become _weaker_ for the melting point to decrease down the group?

   f) Over what _temperatures ranges_ would you expect i) Rubidium, ii) Potassium, to be liquids?

5) _Explain why_ a freshly cut piece of sodium would have a shiny surface, but after a while it would turn white.

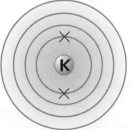

6) _Complete_ the table below, then answer the following questions:

Alkali Metal	No. of Protons	No. of Neutrons	No. of Electrons	Atomic Number	Mass Number
Lithium				3	7
Sodium	11				23
Potassium	19	20			
Rubidium				37	85
Caesium	55				133

   a) _Draw_ an atom of sodium showing its electron arrangement.

   b) _How many_ electrons has sodium in its outer shell?

   c) Why does this make sodium so _reactive_?

   d) What has to happen to an atom of sodium for it to achieve a _full_ outer shell?

   e) What is the _charge_ of a sodium ion? _Explain_ your answer.

   f) When sodium bonds, it changes from an atom to an ion. What is meant by the term "_ion_"?

7) Shown below are two diagrams of atoms.

   a) _Complete_ the atoms by adding the correct number of electrons in each shell.

   b) How can lithium and potassium _gain_ a full outer shell of electrons?

   c) What would the _charge_ on the ions be?

   d) _Write_ the _symbol_ for each ion formed.

   e) In general, the further away the outer electron from the nucleus, the easier it is to remove. Which of lithium and potassium would you expect to be _more reactive_? Explain your answer.

Lithium $^{7}_{3}$Li   Potassium $^{39}_{19}$K

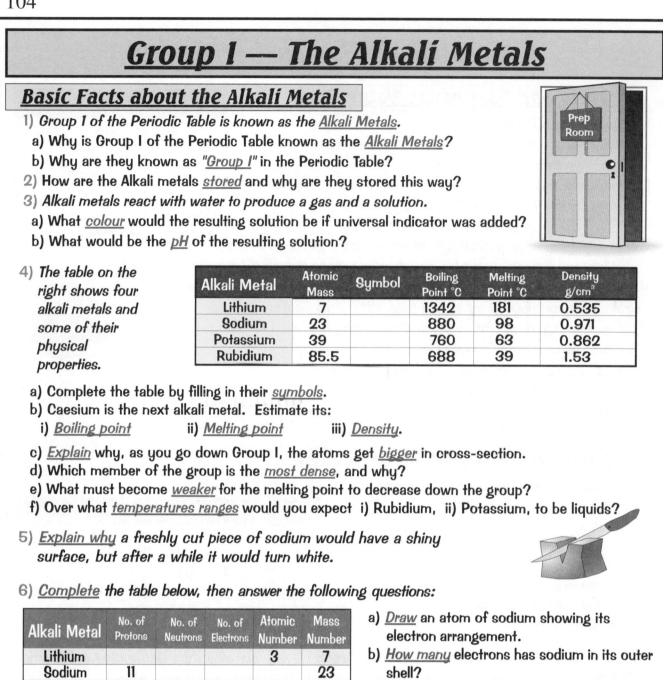

Group 1 — The Alkali Metals

Reactions of Group 1

8) Put the metals in the box in order of reactivity — the most reactive first.

> Caesium, Potassium, Lithium, Sodium, Rubidium.

9) Match up the alkali metal to its reaction in water:

A) Potassium	1) Ignites with yellow/orange flame, fizzes vigorously.
B) Sodium	2) No flame, but fizzes.
C) Lithium	3) Pops and ignites with a lilac flame, fizzes very vigorously.

10) *When an alkali metal reacts with water, a gas is produced.*

   a) *Name* the gas that is produced.
   b) How could you test for this gas?
   c) *Complete* the equations to the right.

   Sodium + Water → [   ]
   Lithium + Water → [   ]

   d) i) *Complete* and *balance* this equation: $K_{(s)} + H_2O_{(l)} \rightarrow KOH_{(aq)} +$ [   ]

   ii) What do the symbols (s), (l), (aq), and (g) stand for in chemical equations?

11) Name *two ions* present in an aqueous solution of potassium hydroxide.

12) *Lithium burns in air to form lithium oxide.*

   a) i) Using the diagrams, *explain* how this happens.
   ii) *Write* the formula of the compound lithium oxide.

   iii) *Complete* the equations below and balance them:

| Lithium + oxygen → [   ] | Li + O_2 → [   ] |
| Sodium + oxygen → [   ] | Na + O_2 → [   ] |

   b) All the alkali metals in Group 1 would react in a similar way with oxygen and water. *Explain* why this is so.

13) *Complete* the table below with the given words and sentences.

> tarnishes quickly to give an oxide layer   tarnishes slowly to give oxide layer
> tarnishes very quickly to give oxide layer   orange   lilac   red

	Colour of flame when burnt	Reaction of the Metal in Air
Lithium		
Sodium		
Potassium		

14) Rubidium and caesium are very dangerous.
   a) *Predict* how these react with *water*.
   b) *Predict* how these react with *air*.
   c) Why are these two metals so reactive?

Top Tips:
With only *one* electron in their outer shell, these metals *haven't got much to lose* — so they're pretty *reactive*. The Exam's most likely to ask about *trends* in the group — so make sure you know how *size*, *reactivity*, *softness*, *density* and *melting* and *boiling points* vary down the group — and *why*.

SECTION SIX — PERIODIC TRENDS

Group VII — The Halogens

Basic Properties of the Halogens

1) Why are the halogens known as the Group VII elements?

2) _Complete_ the table below and answer the questions.

Halogen	Number of electrons in outer shell	State at room temperature	Colour at room temperature	Symbol
Fluorine	7			
Chlorine		gas		
Bromine			brown	
Iodine				I

a) Bromine is a brown volatile liquid. What is meant by _volatile_?

b) Why are the atoms _bigger_ as you go _down_ the group?

c) How does the _reactivity_ change down the group?

3) Under atmospheric pressure, chlorine's melting point is –101°C, and its boiling point is –35°C. Between what temperatures would chlorine be a) a Solid   b) a Liquid   c) a Gas?

4) _Look at the information in the table._

a) From the information given, _estimate_ the melting point of iodine.

b) _Describe_ the patterns (trends) in the melting and boiling points down the group.

Halogen	Melting Point °C	Boiling Point °C
Fluorine	-220	-188
Chlorine	-101	-35
Bromine	-7	58
Iodine		184

5) _Fluorine is an atom with this chemical symbol_ $\rightarrow \; {}^{19}_{9}F$

a) _Draw_ an atom of fluorine from the information given.

b) On your diagram _write down_   i) the number of protons   ii) the number of neutrons
                                                            iii) the number of electrons iv) the electronic configuration.

6) _All the halogens form diatomic molecules._

a) _Explain_ what is meant by _diatomic_.

b) _Write_ the formula for: i) the chlorine molecule   ii) the iodine molecule.

7) _The diagram on the left shows an atom of chlorine._

a) _Draw_ a _molecule_ of chlorine using this atom to help you.

b) What type of bonding do we call this?

Atom of Chlorine

Another Type of Bond...

8) _The Halogens also form another type of bond by gaining one electron._

a) What is this type of bonding called?

b) What would be the charge on a halogen ion?

c) _Name_ a compound in which chlorine would gain an electron.

d) _Name_ a compound in which chlorine would share an electron.

9) _Draw_ the atomic structure and write the _names of the compounds_ formed when:

a) Fluorine combines with lithium,   b) Chlorine combines with hydrogen.

10) _State_ what type of bonding is found in the following halogen compounds:

a) Hydrogen fluoride, HF b) Lithium chloride, LiCl c) Tetrachloromethane d) Potassium bromide.

How can you tell the type of bonding in each? Is there a general rule you followed?

11) Fill in the spaces to _complete_ this table:

Halogen	Symbol	No. of Protons	No. of Neutrons	No. of Electrons	Atomic Mass	Atomic Number
Fluorine	F				19	9
Chlorine	Cl	17	18		35	
Bromine	Br	35			80	
Iodine	I				127	53
Astatine	At	85			210	

Group VII — The Halogens

Chemical Behaviour of the Halogens

12) The reactivity of the halogens decreases down the group, but the reactivity of the alkali metals increases down the group. *Explain* this difference.

13) Iodine can change easily from a dark grey solid to a purple vapour. It does not become a liquid. What do we call this change?

14) Halogens react with metals to form salts.

a) What is a salt?

b) Bearing in mind that Halogens are poisonous, where should reactions of metals and halogens be carried out?

c) *Write in* the salts formed from the following reactions:

d) Are the salts ionic or covalent compounds? *Explain* your answer.

Iron + Chlorine	→	
Aluminium + Bromine	→	
Tin + Chlorine	→	

Silver Halides

15) Most halides are soluble, but *silver halides* are not (e.g. silver chloride). They can be used to test for halide salts because they produce coloured insoluble precipitates.

a) What does the term *"precipitate"* mean?

b) What symbol shows a precipitate in a reaction?

c) *Match* the silver halide to the colour of the precipitate formed:

d) *Look at the reaction below.*

Silver Halide	→	Precipitate
silver chloride		yellow
silver bromide		white
silver iodide		creamy colour

Silver nitrate + Sodium chloride → Silver chloride + Sodium nitrate

Write equations for the reaction of *silver nitrate* with: i) *sodium bromide* ii) *sodium iodide*.

e) What do we call reactions like this where one part of a compound is replaced by another?

16) What effect will chlorine gas have on damp, blue litmus paper?

17) You are given a sample of a solid compound marked **X**, and told it is a halide salt. *Explain* how you could carry out an experiment to find which halide is present in **X**.

Reactivity of Halogens

18) Chlorine is bubbled through sodium bromide as shown in the diagram.

a) What would you see happening in the test tube?

b) Which of chlorine or bromine is the most reactive?

c) How can you *explain* the results of the reaction?

d) *Write* an equation to explain the reaction.

e) *Complete* the equations below by writing the symbols and balancing them.

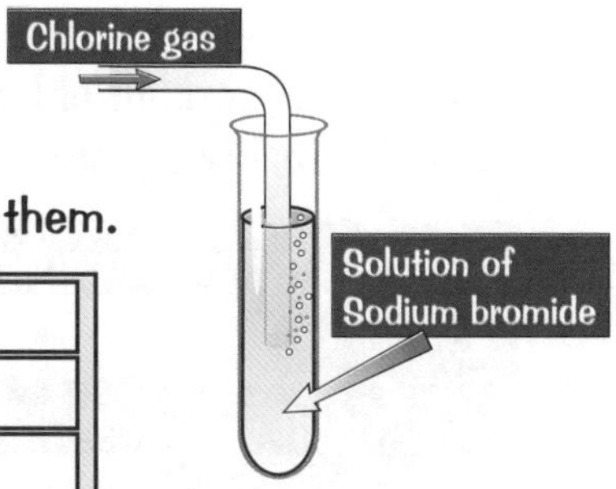

Chlorine gas

Solution of Sodium bromide

i) Fluorine + Sodium iodide	→	
ii) Chlorine + Sodium bromide	→	
iii) Chlorine + Potassium fluoride	→	
iv) Bromine + Potassium iodide	→	

f) What is the general name given to the types of reactions shown above?

Top Tips:

The halogens' reactivity varies in the *opposite* way to group I — make sure you understand *why*. And learn how *size*, *colour* and *melting and boiling points* vary down the group. Then all you need to know is their *dangers*, how you'd *test* for them, and their *displacement reactions* — they could all be in the Exam.

Industrial Salt

Rock Salt

1) Rock salt is a mixture of salt and sand and is mined from underground. It is possible to obtain a pure sample of salt from rock salt in the laboratory. Put the following in the *order* they would be carried out to obtain a *pure* sample of salt.

| i) Filter the solution of rock salt | ii) Solid salt is left in the evaporating basin |

iii) Evaporate the water over a Bunsen burner   iv) Dissolve the rock salt in water

v) Warm the water to increase the solubility of the salt

vi) Sand is left on the filter paper   vii) Place the solution of salt into an evaporating basin

2) State the main *use* of solid rock salt, especially important in the *winter months*?

3) Where are large *salt deposits* found in the UK?

4) *How* is most of the salt obtained from the ground?

5) What is the *common name* for concentrated sodium chloride solution?

Salt Solutions

6) Heating increases the amount of salt that can be dissolved in a given volume of water.

a) What is a *saturated solution*?

b) The graph shows the solubility of two salts. Which salt is the most soluble at:
   i) *low temperatures*   ii) *high temperatures*.

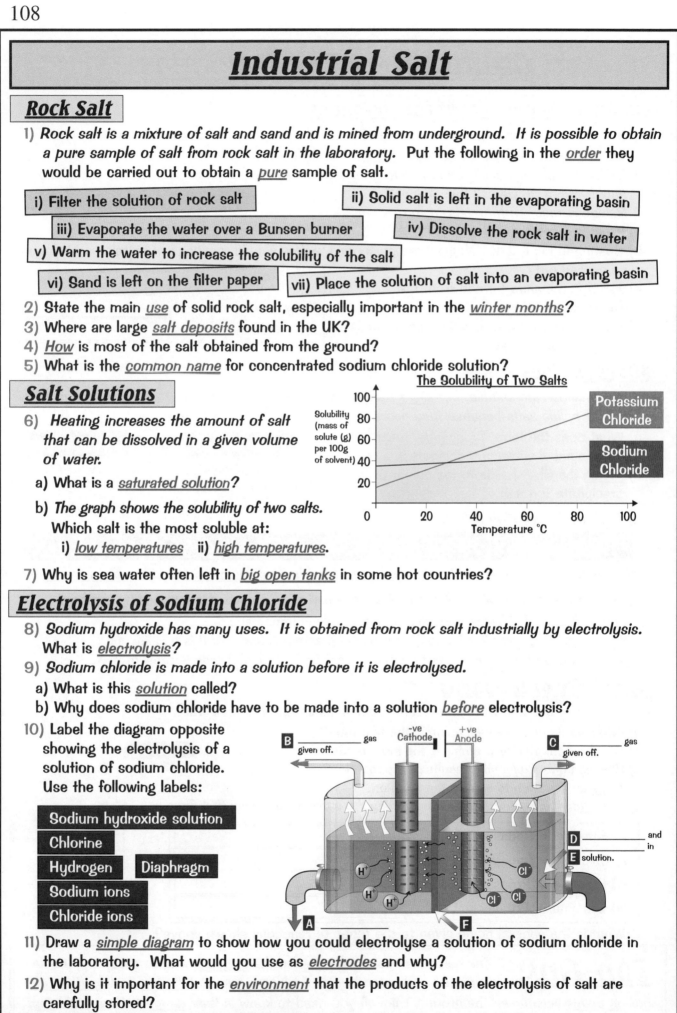

7) Why is sea water often left in *big open tanks* in some hot countries?

Electrolysis of Sodium Chloride

8) Sodium hydroxide has many uses. It is obtained from rock salt industrially by electrolysis. What is *electrolysis*?

9) Sodium chloride is made into a solution before it is electrolysed.

a) What is this *solution* called?

b) Why does sodium chloride have to be made into a solution *before* electrolysis?

10) Label the diagram opposite showing the electrolysis of a solution of sodium chloride. Use the following labels:

Sodium hydroxide solution

Chlorine

Hydrogen   Diaphragm

Sodium ions

Chloride ions

11) Draw a *simple diagram* to show how you could electrolyse a solution of sodium chloride in the laboratory. What would you use as *electrodes* and why?

12) Why is it important for the *environment* that the products of the electrolysis of salt are carefully stored?

13) In this electrolysis process why is sodium *not* produced at the cathode?

Industrial Salt

14) *Complete* the following sentences by *filling in* the missing words (words can be used once, more than once or not at all).

brine	electrolysis	hydrogen	lose	Na^+	chlorine atoms	rocksalt
sodium hydroxide	Cl^-	chlorine molecule	Cl^- ions	gain	hydrogen molecule
industrial	Cl	chlorine	chloride	H^+	hydrogen atoms	industrially

Sodium chloride has many _____ uses. Salt is mined as _____ _____. This is purified to give sodium chloride. Useful products are obtained from a solution of sodium chloride called _____ by _____. The ions produced are H^+, OH^-, _____ and _____. At the anode the _____ ions are deposited. They _____ electrons and become _____ atoms. Two _____ _____ join together to form a _____ _____. At the cathode the _____ ions are deposited. They _____ an electron and become a _____ atom. Two _____ _____ join together to form a _____ _____. All the products from the electrolysis of brine can be used, as _____ _____ solution is left in the reaction vessel.

Ions, Molecules and Atoms in Electrolysis

15) *Complete* and balance this equation to show the formation of a hydrogen molecule:

$$H^+ + _____ \rightarrow _____$$

16) *Draw* the electronic structure of the following transformations occurring during the electrolysis of sodium chloride:

| Sodium ion $\rightarrow$ Sodium atom | Chloride ion $\rightarrow$ Chlorine atom |

17) Why do hydrogen and chlorine atoms need to form molecules before they are given off at the electrodes?

18) *Look* at the equations below. Are they *oxidation* or *reduction* reactions?

i) $Cl^- \rightarrow Cl + e^-$ ii) $H^+ + e^- \rightarrow H$

19) *Chlorine and hydrogen are formed by the electrolysis of brine. If a test tube of each were collected, how could you* test *which contained the chlorine and which the hydrogen (other than by looking at their colour)?*

Molten Sodium Chloride

20) *Sodium chloride doesn't have to be dissolved to separate it.*

a) With the help of a *diagram*, *explain* how else sodium chloride can be separated.

b) Why would this be difficult in a school laboratory?

21) *There are two ions present in the electrolysis of molten sodium chloride.*

a) *Name* these two ions.

b) How is it possible to produce sodium metal by this process but *not* sodium hydroxide?

22) *A diaphragm separates the anode and the cathode in the electrolysis apparatus.* Why *is this important?*

Top Tips:
You probably already knew salt's main uses — except for the *electrolysis* bit. Pity that's the bit you really *need* to know. Make sure you learn the *three* products and exactly *how* they're produced. And don't forget where the salt *comes from*.

Uses of Halogens and Salt Products

Uses of Chlorine

1) *Chlorine is used in bleach. Bleach is made by dissolving chlorine in sodium hydroxide solution. This is the reaction:*

$$Cl_{2 (g)} + NaOH_{(aq)} \rightarrow NaOCl_{(aq)} + NaCl_{(aq)} + H_2O_{(l)}$$

   a) *Balance* the equation.
   b) *Why* is it easy to dissolve chlorine in sodium hydroxide solution?
   c) How could the sodium hyperchlorite, NaOCl, be *separated* from the sodium chloride?

2) *Chlorine is used in the production of tetrachloromethane (CCl$_4$) by reaction with methane.*
   a) *Complete* the diagram opposite by placing **X**s for the electrons in the outer shells of the chlorine atoms.
   b) What *type* of bonding does this represent?
   c) What is tetrachloromethane *used* for?

3) Give *two* other uses of chlorine.

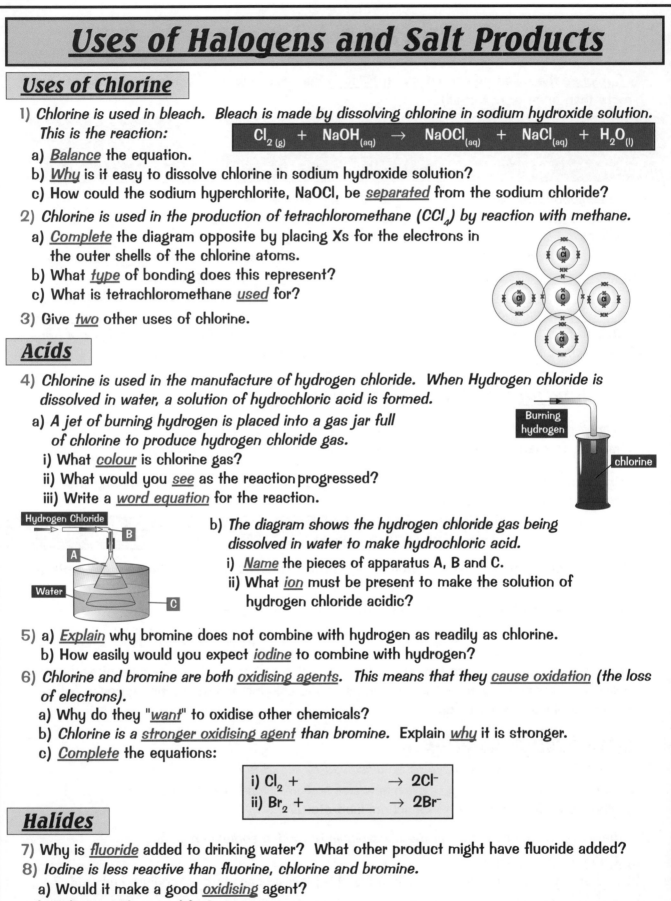

Acids

4) *Chlorine is used in the manufacture of hydrogen chloride. When Hydrogen chloride is dissolved in water, a solution of hydrochloric acid is formed.*
   a) *A jet of burning hydrogen is placed into a gas jar full of chlorine to produce hydrogen chloride gas.*
   i) What *colour* is chlorine gas?
   ii) What would you *see* as the reaction progressed?
   iii) Write a *word equation* for the reaction.

   b) *The diagram shows the hydrogen chloride gas being dissolved in water to make hydrochloric acid.*
   i) *Name* the pieces of apparatus **A**, **B** and **C**.
   ii) What *ion* must be present to make the solution of hydrogen chloride acidic?

5) a) *Explain* why bromine does not combine with hydrogen as readily as chlorine.
   b) How easily would you expect *iodine* to combine with hydrogen?

6) *Chlorine and bromine are both oxidising agents. This means that they cause oxidation (the loss of electrons).*
   a) Why do they "*want*" to oxidise other chemicals?
   b) *Chlorine is a stronger oxidising agent than bromine.* Explain *why* it is stronger.
   c) *Complete* the equations:

   i) Cl$_2$ + _____ → 2Cl⁻
   ii) Br$_2$ + _____ → 2Br⁻

Halides

7) Why is *fluoride* added to drinking water? What other product might have fluoride added?
8) *Iodine is less reactive than fluorine, chlorine and bromine.*
   a) Would it make a good *oxidising* agent?
   b) What is *iodine* used for?

9) *Silver halides are used in photographic film. A sample of silver bromide can be made from a mixture of silver nitrate and sodium bromide.*

   a) *The silver bromide (AgBr) formed is easy to split apart.* *Write an equation* to show this.
   b) Which type of *energy* splits up the silver bromide in photography?

Uses of Halogens and Salt Products

Products from Brine

10) *Electrolysis of brine produces sodium hydroxide, hydrogen and chlorine.*
   a) *Hydrogen is used in the Haber Process. What is <u>produced</u> in the Haber process?*
   b) *Hydrogen burns to release energy. What <u>name</u> is given to materials that do this?*

11) *Hydrogen is used to change oils into fats for making <u>margarine</u>.*
   a) *Butter and lard are saturated fats, while sunflower oil and olive oil are unsaturated fats.*
      i) *What does <u>saturated</u> mean?*
      ii) *What does <u>unsaturated</u> mean?*

   b) *Margarine is made by changing a liquid oil into a solid. This is done by adding hydrogen.*

   What will be <u>made</u> when hydrogen is added to an unsaturated molecule?

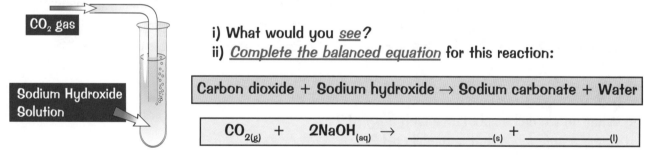

Unsaturated molecule

Sodium Hydroxide

12) Give *three* uses of sodium hydroxide.

13) What is an everyday *name* for sodium hydrogencarbonate?

14) What would happen if *acid* were added to sodium hydrogencarbonate solution?

15) *The diagram shows how sodium carbonate could be made in the laboratory.*

CO$_2$ gas

Sodium Hydroxide Solution

   i) What would you *see*?
   ii) *Complete the balanced equation* for this reaction:

Carbon dioxide + Sodium hydroxide → Sodium carbonate + Water

$$CO_{2(g)} + 2NaOH_{(aq)} \rightarrow \underline{\hspace{3cm}}_{(s)} + \underline{\hspace{3cm}}_{(l)}$$

16) *Sodium hydroxide is a strong alkali. What must sodium hydroxide <u>produce</u> in solution?*

17) *<u>Fill the blanks</u> using the words below. Words can be used once, more than once or not at all:*

sodium hydrogencarbonate hydrogen chloride hydrocarbon sodium hydroxide chlorine ammonia hydrogen fats textiles margarine oven-cleaners

Brine is electrolysed to give the three products _____, _____ and

_____. _____ is used in making PVC, disinfecting drinking water and in

swimming pools. To manufacture PVC it is made into _____, and this is added to a

long chain _____ molecule in such a way as to form PVC. Hydrogen is used to make

_____ such as _____. _____ is used to make soaps

and detergents, _____, paper and _____ such as rayon wool and cotton.

Top Tips: Fairly routine stuff, this — just learning the <u>uses</u> of loads of chemicals. It often helps here to think of the chemical's <u>properties</u> — if you can see <u>why</u> it's good for a particular use, you'll find it much easier to <u>remember</u>. Check you know what's used in these — <u>bleach</u>, <u>margarine</u>, <u>soap</u>, <u>insecticides</u>, <u>ammonia</u>, and <u>antiseptic</u>.

Acids and Alkalis

Is it True or must it be False...

1) *Place* a *tick* in the box next to each of the following statements to indicate which are *True* and which are *False*.

	True	False
All acids are dangerous		
All alkalis are dangerous		
All acids are dissolved in water		
All alkalis are dissolved in water		
Most acids can burn skin		
Alkalis feel soapy		
Acids produce H^+ ions in solution		
Acids taste sweet		
Alkalis produce OH^- ions in solution		
All acids can corrode		
Acids have a pH above 7		
Acids have a pH below 7		
The pH scale goes from 0 to 14		

Common Bench Acids and Alkalis

2) *Give the names* of three common bench acids and alkalis, and write out their formulae:

Name of Acid	Formula of Acid
(i)	
(ii)	
(iii)	

Name of Alkali	Formula of Alkali
(i)	
(ii)	
(iii)	

3) What do we call a substance with a *pH* of 7?

4) *Name a substance* that is usually pH 7.

5) State which of the following is an *acid* and which is an *alkali*:

a) Hydrochloric acid

b) Sodium hydroxide

c) KOH

d) H_2SO_4

e) HNO_3

6) What is an *indicator*?

7) *Why* are indicators useful?

8) What is a base? *Name* three bases.

9) *Complete the table* by adding the correct colour of the indicator in acid or alkali:

Indicator	Colour in solution of:	
	Acid	Alkali
Universal Indicator		
Red Litmus		
Blue Litmus		
Phenolphthalein		
Methyl Orange		
Methyl Red		

Acids and Alkalis

The pH and Universal Indicator Solution

10) _Colour in_ the pH chart with the _correct colours_ for Universal indicator solution:

pH 1 2 3 4 5 6 7 8 9 10 11 12 13 14

ACIDS   ALKALIS

NEUTRAL

11) What values of pH would you expect for .....?

     i) Citric acid   iv) Oven cleaner
     ii) Sodium chloride (common salt)   v) Sodium hydroxide
     iii) Lime (calcium hydroxide)   vi) Hydrochloric acid

12) _Fill in_ the blanks with the correct words:

> Universal indicator turns a _____ colour in strong acids, _____ in neutral solutions and _____ in strong alkalis. Another indicator which changes colour in acid and alkali is _____ .
>
> A solution which is not acid or alkali is said to be _____, and has a pH of _____.
> Lemons and oranges contain _____ acid. Fizzy drinks contain _____ acid.
> Taking milk of magnesia tablets may help indigestion because they contain a weak _____.
> Strong oven cleaners contain a strong alkali called _____ _____.
> Car batteries contain _____ acid.

13) Explain how you could _measure_ the pH of a colourless solution.

14) Explain how you could _measure_ the pH of a brightly-coloured solution.

15) _The labels have fallen off test tubes of vinegar, water, sulphuric acid, and oven cleaner. The table to the right shows the colours observed when pH paper was added to each tube._
   Fill in the missing _pH values_ and _identify_ which substance is in which tube.

Tube	Colour	pH
1	Red	
2	Orange	
3	Green	
4	Blue	

Uses of Acids

16) Match the acid with where it is found or used:

Acid	Found in / used for
Methanoic	Lead acid batteries
Ethanoic	Ant stings
Sulphuric	Pickling onions
Carbonic	Stomach acid
Hydrochloric	Fizzy drinks
Tartaric	Lemons
Citric	Grapes

Top Tips:
This stuff's not so bad, I'd say — just loads of _H+_ and _OH-_ ions floating about. But make sure you can define an _acid_ and _alkali_ in terms of these — and write an equation for their _neutralisation_. If you can do that and know your _pH scale_, you're pretty much there...

Acid Reactions

General Reactions of Acids

1) Complete the following general acid reactions by filling in the missing products.

> Acid + Base → A Salt + _____
>
> Acid + Metal → A Salt + _____
>
> Acid + Metal Carbonate → A Salt + Water + _____ _____
>
> Acid + Metal Hydrogencarbonate → A _____ + Water + Carbon dioxide

2) What is an alkali?

3) What is a base?

4) *Give* a *definition* of a salt.

5) *Link up* the words in the diagram opposite to show the salt produced by each acid.

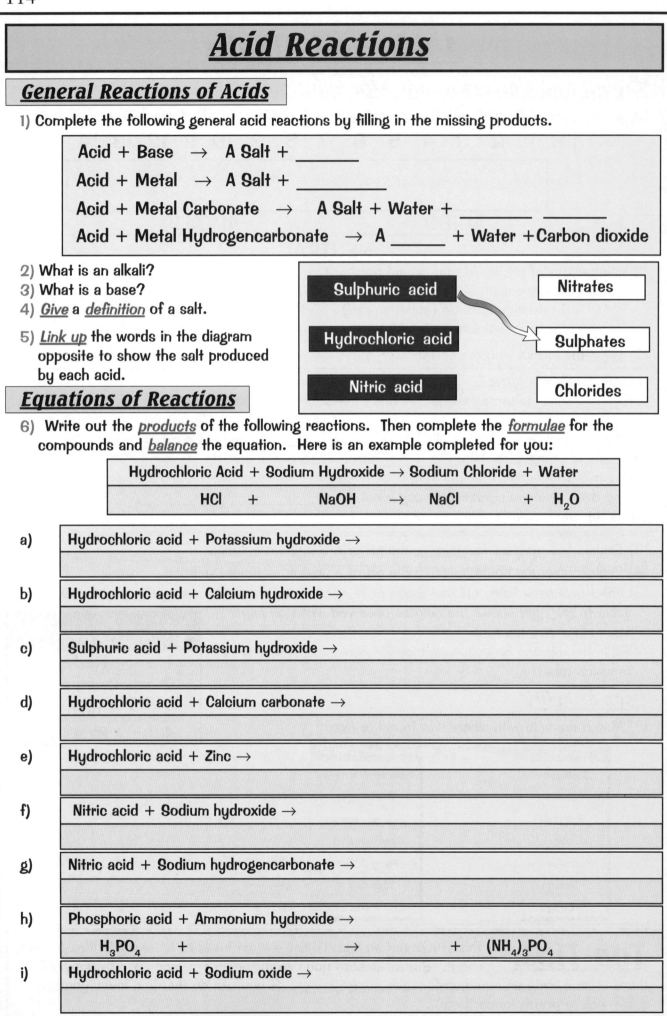

Sulphuric acid	Nitrates
Hydrochloric acid	Sulphates
Nitric acid	Chlorides

Equations of Reactions

6) Write out the *products* of the following reactions. Then complete the *formulae* for the compounds and *balance* the equation. Here is an example completed for you:

| Hydrochloric Acid + Sodium Hydroxide → Sodium Chloride + Water |
| HCl + NaOH → NaCl + H₂O |

$$\text{HCl} \quad + \quad \text{NaOH} \quad \rightarrow \quad \text{NaCl} \quad + \quad \text{H}_2\text{O}$$

a) Hydrochloric acid + Potassium hydroxide →

b) Hydrochloric acid + Calcium hydroxide →

c) Sulphuric acid + Potassium hydroxide →

d) Hydrochloric acid + Calcium carbonate →

e) Hydrochloric acid + Zinc →

f) Nitric acid + Sodium hydroxide →

g) Nitric acid + Sodium hydrogencarbonate →

h) Phosphoric acid + Ammonium hydroxide →

$$\text{H}_3\text{PO}_4 \quad + \quad \quad \rightarrow \quad \quad + \quad (\text{NH}_4)_3\text{PO}_4$$

i) Hydrochloric acid + Sodium oxide →

Acid Reactions

Neutralisation

7) _Answer_ these questions on neutralisation:

  a) What is neutralisation?

  b) Why is neutralisation important to farmers?

  c) What do farmers use to neutralise over-acidic soils?

8) _Two companies advertise pills which they say relieve stomach ache by neutralising excess stomach acid._

  a) _Describe_ what you would do to:

    i) check that the pills do in fact neutralise acid?

    ii) discover which pill neutralised the most acid?

  b) _Magnesium Hydroxide is the active ingredient in some indigestion tablets._
    Write an equation showing how this chemical reacts with acid in the stomach.

9) _Read the following passage, which explains how fire extinguishers work._

> _Red fire extinguishers contain sodium hydrogencarbonate solution. When the plunger is pressed down, sulphuric acid mixes and reacts with the sodium hydrogencarbonate solution, causing a gas to be produced. This makes the pressure build up inside the cylinder, forcing a foam of liquid and bubbles to be squeezed out of the nozzle._

  a) What is the name of the gas?

  b) _Write_ a word equation to show what happens.

10) Use the information opposite to _suggest_ the best remedy for: a) a wasp sting   b) a bee sting   c) nettle sting.

11) Neutralisation is simplified as $H^+_{(aq)} + OH^-_{(aq)} \rightarrow H_2O_{(l)}$
  Explain where the H^+ and OH^- come from.

> - Wasp stings are basic.
> - Bee stings are acidic.
> - Nettles stings are acidic.
> - Bicarbonate of soda is alkaline.
> - Dock leaves contain alkali.
> - Lemon juice is acidic.

Making Salts
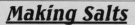

12) _Describe_ how you might produce a dry sample of the salt _copper sulphate_ using copper oxide, sulphuric acid and normal lab apparatus.

13) Which acid and which other chemical would you use to make ..... ?

    a) Sodium chloride   b) Copper chloride   c) Potassium sulphate

    d) Zinc sulphate   e) Ammonium nitrate   f) Ammonium sulphate

14) Why is it a _bad idea_ to use sodium and hydrochloric acid to make sodium chloride?

Top Tips: All these reactions might seem a bit complicated — but there's basically only _four types_. If you can write equations for _bases_, _metals_, _metal carbonates_ and _metal hydrogencarbonates_, you'll sail through. But make sure you can work out the _salt_ produced when something's _neutralised_ — write out the equation if you're not sure.

Metals

Properties of Metals

1) *Aluminium and lead are both metals.* <u>*Explain*</u> *why aluminium has a lower density than lead.*

2) *Metals have a type of bonding known as a <u>metallic bond</u>.*

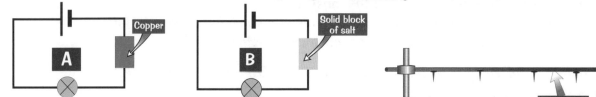

   a) Label the diagram opposite showing positive and negative particles, and explain what you understand by <u>metallic bonding</u>.
   b) What are the names of the <u>negative</u> particles?
   c) Name a <u>property</u> that these particles give to metals.

3) In the circuits below, which bulb A or B would light? <u>*Explain*</u> *your answer in detail.*

4) *The experiment on the right was set up to show heat transfer along a piece of copper.*
   a) <u>*Name*</u> *a suitable substance that would hold the drawing pins to the copper.*
   b) What would happen to the drawing pins as the copper wire is heated?
   c) <u>*Name*</u> *this type of heat transfer.*
   d) <u>*Draw a diagram*</u> *to <u>explain</u> how heat is transferred in this way through a piece of copper.*
   e) What <u>term</u> is used to describe any material that does not allow heat to flow through it?
   f) What would you <u>*expect to happen*</u> *if aluminium were tested in the same way? Why?*

5) *Metals have a high "tensile strength".*
   a) What does this <u>mean</u>?   b) <u>*Why*</u> *does this make them useful?*

6) *Many elements occur naturally.*
   a) Approximately <u>*what proportion*</u> *of the naturally occurring elements are metals?*
   b) Would you find a positive or negative <u>charge</u> on a metal ion?

7) *Why are metals good at <u>conducting electricity</u>? (Answer in terms of their metallic structure).*

8) *Metals are "hard".*
   a) <u>*Explain*</u> *what uses they have because of their hardness.*
   b) You are given 4 metals; copper, silver, lead and aluminium. <u>*Describe*</u> *a test you could carry out to show the order of their hardness.*

More Questions on Properties of Metals

9) *Below is a table of the density and electrical conductivity of five metals. Use it to answer the questions opposite.*

   a) <u>*List them*</u> *in order of density (highest first).*
   b) <u>*List them*</u> *in order of conductivity (highest first).*
   c) Which metal is the most useful for wiring a house? <u>*Explain*</u> *your answer <u>fully</u>.*
   d) Which metal is the most useful for building an aircraft? <u>*Explain*</u> *your answer.*
   e) An alloy is a mixture of copper (4%) and aluminium (96%). Will its density be <u>*greater*</u> *or <u>less</u> than the density of aluminium? Explain your answer.*

Metal	Density (g/cm³)	Electrical Cond. (Relative Units)
Copper	8.9	5.9
Lead	11.3	4.8
Aluminium	2.7	3.8
Iron	7.9	1.0
Zinc	7.1	1.7

Metals

More on Physical Properties of Metals

10) *Melting and boiling points of metals are generally high.*
a) How does this make them useful?
b) Which metal is the main exception to this? Give one use of it because of this property.

11) *Metals are malleable.* What does *malleable* mean and where could this property be useful?

12) *In a laboratory, the tensile strength of metals can be tested.*

a) *Explain* a simple test you would use. What precautions would you need to take?
b) How could you ensure it was a *fair* test?

Uses of Metals

13) *Match up* each metal to its use:

1. Copper	A. Used for jewellery
2. Lead	B. Used for aircraft
3. Aluminium	C. Used for wiring
4. Gold	D. Used to keep out radiation

14) a) Complete the table below, showing properties and associated uses for the above four metals. The first one has been done for you.

Metal	Property	Use
Copper	Conducts electricity	Household wiring
Lead		
Aluminium		
Gold		

b) What is the name given to a *mixture of metals*?
c) *Why* do we mix metals together?
d) *How* is this done?
e) Why is this called a mixture and *not* a compound?

15) *Using the table opposite answer these questions:*

a) *Explain* why tungsten is used in light bulbs.
b) *Draw* a bar chart showing the melting points of the metals in the table.

Metal	Melting Point (°C)
Aluminium	659
Copper	1083
Gold	1064
Iron	1540
Lead	328
Tin	232
Tungsten	3410

Questions on Chemical Behaviour...

16) *Explain* what the term *reducing agent* means. *Why* are metals reducing agents?

17) *Explain why* gold does not tarnish easily and is found as an element on its own.

18) How does the *pH* of metallic oxides compare to that of non-metallic oxides?

Top Tips: Metallic bonding's due to *free electrons* — and the bonds are usually pretty *strong*. That about sums metals up, I'd say. Make sure you understand how this affects their conduction of *heat* and *electricity* — and their *melting and boiling points*. Other than that, just make sure you can define an *alloy* — and give *examples*.

SECTION SIX — PERIODIC TRENDS

Non-Metals

Non-Metals in the Periodic Table

1) *Look at the Periodic Table opposite.*

   a) *Shade in* the area that represents non-metals.

   b) Use a *different colour* to shade the group that's all gases at room temperature.

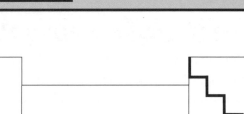

2) *Look at the table below, then complete parts a) - d):*

Element	Symbol	Melting Point (°C)	Boiling Point (°C)	State at RTP
Sulphur		112	444	
Oxygen		-218	-183	
Bromine		-7	58	
Neon		-248	-246	
Iodine		114	183	

   a) Write in the symbol of each element.

   b) Write in the state of each element at room temperature and pressure (RTP).

   c) Which non-metal is a liquid at RTP?

   d) In which state would you find the majority of non-metals at RTP?

Properties of Non-Metals

3) *Iron is a metal and sulphur is a non-metal.* <u>*Complete*</u> the table below for both, showing the differences between metals and non-metals. Use the words in the box.

> poor conductor   low   good conductor
> malleable   high   brittle

Element	Conducts heat	Conducts electricity	Melting Point	Boiling Point	Strength	Density
Iron						
Sulphur						

4) *Most non-metals do not conduct electricity.*

   a) What is the general name given to non-conducting materials?

   b) Explain why non-metals *do not* conduct electricity.

   c) Name an *exception* to this rule.

5) *Answer these questions on bondings between non-metal elements:*

   a) What type of *bonding* do you get between two non-metal elements?

   b) *Explain* why this is so.

6) *Non-metals form small molecules whilst metals bond in giant metallic structures.*

   Give two *properties* that each have because of their structures.

7) *Many non-metals form diatomic molecules.*

   a) What is a *diatomic* molecule?

   b) Apart from oxygen name *two other* non-metals which could form diatomic molecules.

   c) Draw a *dot and cross* diagram for a molecule of oxygen. (Oxygen — $^{16}_{8}O$)

8) *Hydrogen is a non-metal. The structure of an atom of hydrogen is drawn below. Hydrogen is a gas at room temperature and pressure, and it shares a number of properties with non-metals. However, it could be argued that hydrogen be placed in* <u>Group I</u> *of the Periodic Table.* <u>*Explain*</u> *why this is so.*

9) What type of *bonding* does hydrogen form with oxygen?

10) *Carbon and iodine sublime.*

   What does this *mean*?

Non-Metals

Atoms of Non-Metals

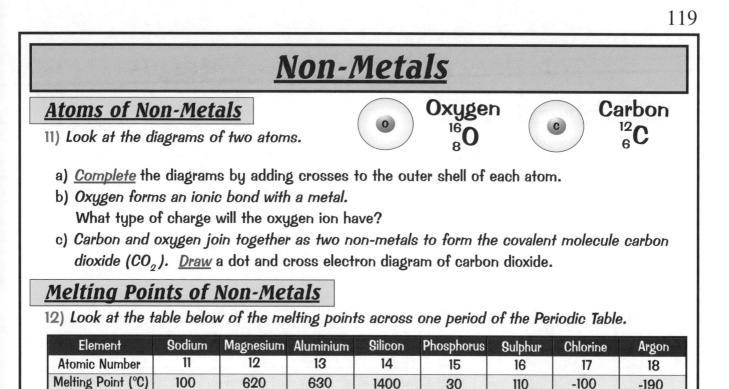

11) *Look at the diagrams of two atoms.*

a) <u>Complete</u> the diagrams by adding crosses to the outer shell of each atom.

b) *Oxygen forms an ionic bond with a metal.*
What type of charge will the oxygen ion have?

c) *Carbon and oxygen join together as two non-metals to form the covalent molecule carbon dioxide (CO_2). <u>Draw</u> a dot and cross electron diagram of carbon dioxide.*

Melting Points of Non-Metals

12) *Look at the table below of the melting points across one period of the Periodic Table.*

Element	Sodium	Magnesium	Aluminium	Silicon	Phosphorus	Sulphur	Chlorine	Argon
Atomic Number	11	12	13	14	15	16	17	18
Melting Point (°C)	100	620	630	1400	30	110	-100	-190

a) Using the information given, <u>plot a graph</u> of the melting points against atomic number across the period.

b) <u>Explain</u> any trends you see in your graph.

c) Are there any results that seem unusual. <u>Suggest a reason</u> for this.

d) Using your knowledge of atomic structure which element listed would you expect to have the <u>weakest attraction</u> between atoms? Why?

Carbon and Silicon and Non-Metal Oxides

13) *Silicon and carbon can form giant structures.*
Why is this unusual for non-metals?

14) *These two diagrams show the structures of graphite and diamond:*

.....*two forms of carbon.*

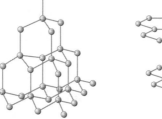
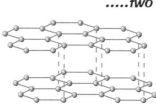

a) What do we call the <u>different forms</u> in which a <u>single element</u> can exist?

b) *Graphite and diamond show different properties.*
<u>Giving reasons</u>, state which of the two you think show the following properties:
  i) Conducts electricity.   ii) Is a hard material.   iii) Is a soft material.

c) Give one industrial use of diamond and one industrial use of graphite.

15) *Non-metal oxides such as SO_2 and NO_2 are often released into the atmosphere.*

a) What <u>substances</u> would these make if mixed with water?

b) Why is their release into the atmosphere a problem, and what's the common name for this phenomenon?

Top Tips: Exams questions often compare <u>non-metals</u> with metals. Just make sure you understand <u>why</u> non-metals are made of <u>molecules</u> — and <u>how</u> this affects their <u>properties</u>. And you must know how and why <u>diamond</u> and <u>graphite</u> differ.

The Reactivity Series of Metals

The Reactivity of Metals

1) *The reactivity series is a list of metals.*
   a) What do you _understand_ by the term "reactivity series"?
   b) Some metals corrode in air. What is meant by _corrosion_?
   c) *Metals react with air, water and acids.* What might you look for in such reactions to identify which is the _most reactive_ metal?
   d) Put these metals in order of reactivity, starting with the most reactive first:

   | potassium | gold | aluminium | silver | lead | sodium | iron | copper | zinc |

   e) _Match_ the following metals to the correct statement.

1) Potassium	A) Will not react with water or dilute acid
2) Copper	B) Found alone not combined with anything
3) Iron	C) Very reactive metal
4) Gold	D) Corrodes in air fairly easily forming a substance called rust

2) Between which elements are i) carbon and ii) hydrogen, in the reactivity series?

3) *Potassium has one electron in its outer shell, which is lost easily.*
   a) Whereabouts in the _reactivity series_ would you expect to find potassium?
   b) _Name_ two elements that could be above potassium in the reactivity series.
   c) Using the information given below, _place_ metals X and Y in the correct position in the reactivity series to the right.

   | Potassium |
   | Magnesium |
   | Iron |
   | Gold |
   | Platinum |

   Metal X — Very reactive, burns in air readily to form a layer of oxide. Reacts violently in water but does not ignite the hydrogen produced.

   Metal Y — Corrodes very slowly, needs carbon for extraction from ore.

4) *Look at the following:* Sodium $^{23}_{11}$Na , Magnesium $^{24}_{12}$Mg

   a) _Draw_ an atom of sodium and magnesium. How many electrons has each to _lose_ to gain a full shell?
   b) Looking at the atomic structure of these metals, _why_ is magnesium less reactive than sodium?

Electrolysis

5) *Potassium, sodium, calcium, magnesium and aluminium all need to be extracted from their ores by electrolysis.*

   a) What is an "_ore_"?
   b) Why do these metals need to be extracted by _electrolysis_?

6) *The diagram opposite shows the electrolysis of aluminium ore.*

   a) What is _aluminium ore_ called?
   b) To extract aluminium, the ore has to be _melted_. Why is this?
   c) Which type of _energy_ is used to split up the ore?
   d) *Aluminium forms ions Al^{3+}.* _Complete_ this ionic equation to show what will happen at the negative electrode to give pure aluminium.

   Positive Electrode

   Negative Electrode

   Molten Aluminium

   $$Al^{3+} + \underline{\hspace{2cm}} \rightarrow \underline{\hspace{2cm}}$$

   e) Why is it _impossible_ to extract aluminium from its ore using carbon?

The Reactivity Series of Metals

The Blast Furnace

7) The diagram on the right shows the Blast Furnace used to convert iron ore to iron. Coke burns to form CO_2 which then reacts with more coke to make carbon monoxide. The carbon monoxide is a reducing agent and reacts with iron ore (Fe_2O_3) to make iron.

$$Fe_2O_3 + 3CO \rightarrow 2Fe + 3CO_2$$

a) What is a _reducing agent_?

b) _Where_ is carbon in the reactivity series relative to iron?

c) _Explain_ how the carbon monoxide reduces the iron ore.

d) _Write_ a word equation for the reaction given above.

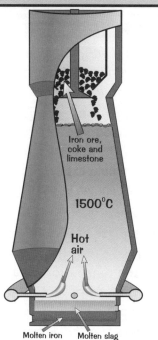

Iron ore, coke and limestone

1500°C

Hot air

Molten iron   Molten slag

Extracting Metals from the Earth

8) Silver, gold and platinum are found _native_ in the ground as elements and not as compounds.
Explain how this can happen.

9) Aluminium is much more _abundant_ in the Earth's crust than iron, yet it is much _more expensive_ to buy.
Explain why it is so expensive, in terms of its reactivity and the cost of extracting it from its ore.

Reactions of Metals

10) Why do you think gold and silver can be worn next to the skin as jewellery, but other metals like sodium cannot?

11) Metals are shiny. They do however become "dull" with time.

a) _Name_ a metal that would become _dull_ if left in air for only a short time.

b) _Name_ a metal that would _not_ become _dull_ easily in air.

c) _Write down_ the name of the product in (a).

12) The table opposite contains information about metals.

a) _Complete the table_, using your own words to explain what happens when each metal is heated in air.

b) _Write_ a balanced equation for the reaction of the following with air (you'll need to work out which element in the air they react with first):

  i) Iron.

  ii) Calcium.

  iii) Sodium.

c) From your results in (a) _write a list_ of the order of reactivity, starting with the most reactive.

Metal	Reaction when heated in air	Compound formed
Calcium		
Zinc		
Iron		
Copper	slow reaction	
Silver		
Potassium		
Gold		
Magnesium		
Platinum	no reaction	
Lead		

Top Tips:
A metal's _reactivity_ is basically just how easily its atoms _lose electrons_. It's pretty handy though — so make sure you know it. If you can use it to predict _displacement reactions_ then I'd say you've pretty much got it sussed. Thinking up a _rhyme_ or _mnemonic_ will help you remember it — so try this if you find it hard.

Corrosion of Metals

Corrosion of Iron

1) Iron is a very cheap and useful metal, but it corrodes easily. The experiment shown opposite investigates corrosion of iron.

a) What is the "_common_" name for corroded iron?

b) _Write down_ in the table opposite what you would expect to happen in the test tubes shown in the diagram.

c) _Explain_ the following:

   i) The use of anhydrous calcium chloride.
   ii) The reason the water was boiled.
   iii) The reason for using oil.
   iv) The use of test tube 5 with normal air, in the experiment.

d) What _two things_ must be present for the iron to rust?

e) _Write_ a word equation to show what happened in the tubes where rusting occurred.

1	2	3	4	5
Salt water	Water	Boiled water	Anhydrous calcium chloride	Normal air

Layer of oil

Test tube Number	Observations after one week
1	
2	
3	
4	
5	

Corrosion of Other Metals

2) Sally carried out an experiment to see if other metals corroded as quickly as iron. This is what she set up...

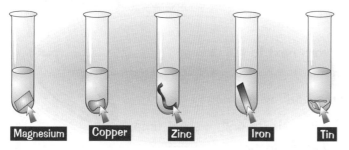

Magnesium   Copper   Zinc   Iron   Tin

Sally put 5cm³ of tap water into each test tube and added 1g of a different metal to each. She then left them in the lab for a week.

a) Why did she ensure that the metal weighed 1g and carefully measured the 5cm³ of water?

b) Which metal(s) would you expect to corrode? _Explain_ your answer.

c) Which metal(s) would you expect to show no change at all?

3) A large treasure chest made of iron was discovered in the sea. It was recovered with surprisingly little rust and brought to the surface. _Explain why_ there was so little rust.

4) _Why_ are steel parts of large ships likely to corrode?

5) Most bikes are made of steel too. What stops them from _rusting quickly_? How?

Stopping the Rusting Process

6) Metals can be treated by galvanising.

a) What is _galvanising_?

b) By what _process_ are metals galvanised?

c) Which _metal_ is used to galvanise iron?

7) Answer these questions on Stainless Steel:

a) What is _stainless_ steel?

b) _Name_ an object you might use every day that is made of stainless steel.

c) Why does stainless steel _not rust_ even though it contains iron?

Corrosion of Metals

Protecting Iron

8) Iron can be protected from rusting by the following methods:

| oiling or greasing the iron | galvanising | painting | coating with aluminium |

a) Which of the above _methods_ do you think will give iron the best protection from rusting? _Explain_ your answer.

b) Why is the best method _not_ always used?

9) _The following apparatus investigates the protecting of iron:_

a) In _which_ tubes would you expect to see the iron rust?

b) In which tubes would the iron _not_ rust?

c) In the tubes where the iron does not rust, _what_ would you expect to see?

d) _Complete_ the following sentences by crossing out the incorrect words.

> For this kind of protection to work the metal touching the iron must be (more/less) reactive than iron. The metal corrodes (in preference to/as well as) iron. This is called (sacrificial protection/non-sacrificial protection).

f) _Normally iron must form ions like Fe^{3+} to form rust — it does this by losing electrons._
   Write an equation for this process: | $Fe \rightarrow$ |

g) In tube A, magnesium forms the ions instead of iron.
   Write an equation to show this: | $Mg \rightarrow$ |

h) _Explain_ in detail how this kind of protection from rust works.

Preventing Corrosion

10) In the table on the right _put a tick_ next to the metals likely to corrode, and _a cross_ next to those that aren't.

	Will corrosion occur?
a) Iron protected by zinc	
b) Aluminium protected by zinc	
c) Zinc protected by aluminium	
d) Copper protected by silver	
e) Magnesium protected by zinc	

11) _Explain_ the answers you gave in question 10) in terms of the reactivities of the metals.

12) _Fill in the missing_ columns in the table on the right, stating the best ways to prevent each object from rusting.

Item	Best way to prevent rusting
a) Gate	
b) Hull of a ship	
c) Car door	
d) Tools	
e) Machinery	

Top Tips: _Corrosion_ of metals nearly always means _oxidation_. Exams usually ask about _iron_ — remember it only rusts with both oxygen _and_ water. Other than that, just make sure you know the main ways to _prevent rust_, and remember that _aluminium_ oxide actually _protects_ the metal — even though aluminium's pretty _reactive_.

Transition Metals

Properties of Transition Metals

1) The transition metals have properties of typical metals.
List the properties you would expect a transition element to have.

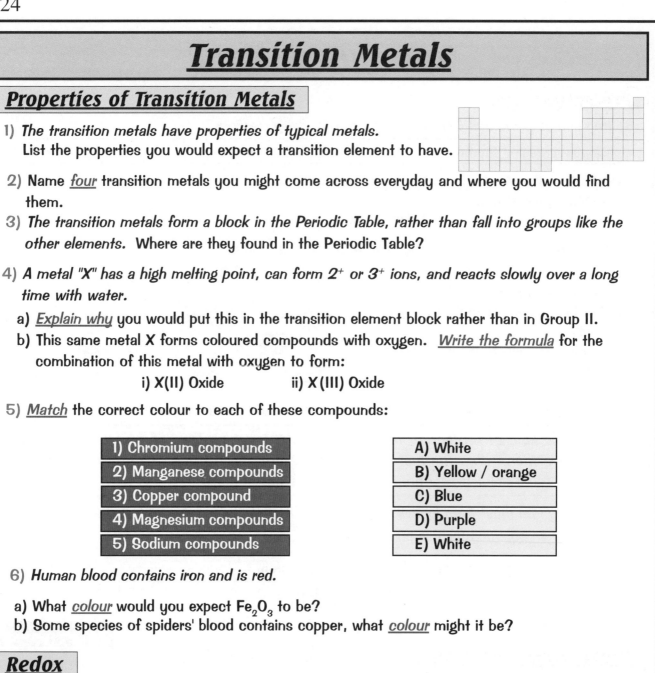

2) Name *four* transition metals you might come across everyday and where you would find them.

3) The transition metals form a block in the Periodic Table, rather than fall into groups like the other elements. Where are they found in the Periodic Table?

4) A metal "**X**" has a high melting point, can form 2^+ or 3^+ ions, and reacts slowly over a long time with water.

a) *Explain why* you would put this in the transition element block rather than in Group II.

b) This same metal **X** forms coloured compounds with oxygen. *Write the formula* for the combination of this metal with oxygen to form:

i) X(II) Oxide   ii) X(III) Oxide

5) *Match* the correct colour to each of these compounds:

1) Chromium compounds	A) White
2) Manganese compounds	B) Yellow / orange
3) Copper compound	C) Blue
4) Magnesium compounds	D) Purple
5) Sodium compounds	E) White

6) Human blood contains iron and is red.

a) What *colour* would you expect Fe_2O_3 to be?
b) Some species of spiders' blood contains copper, what *colour* might it be?

Redox

7) The transition metal elements often have more than just one ion. For example, iron can be Iron(II) — Fe^{2+} or Iron(III) — Fe^{3+}. The number in brackets refers to the metal ion charge.

Write the formula for the following compounds in the table and give the charge on the transition element ion in each case. One has been done for you.

(use the ion table on the inside front cover)

Compound	Formula	Charge on Ion
a) Iron(II) oxide		
b) Iron(III) chloride		
c) Iron(III) bromide	$FeBr_3$	Fe^{3+}
d) Copper(II) oxide		
e) Copper(I) chloride		
f) Copper(II) chloride		
g) Iron(III) iodide		

8) Iron(II) can be easily changed into Iron(III) : Fe^{3+}

a) What *type* of reaction is this?
b) What does *OIL RIG* help you remember about oxidation and reduction?
c) What type of reaction would it be if Fe^{3+} ions were *changed* into Fe^{2+} ions?

Transition Metals

Uses of Transition Metals

9) Answer these questions on the uses of transition metals:
  a) _Give a use_ for each of these transition metals: i) Iron ii) Zinc iii) Copper
  b) Why is copper used for household water pipes in _preference_ to iron or zinc?

10) _Name two_ transition elements that could be made into a permanent magnet.

11) An element Y was discovered and put with the transition metals because of its properties.

  a) _Fill in the table_ below for the element Y, giving details of its general properties (in terms of good, bad, high, low, etc.).

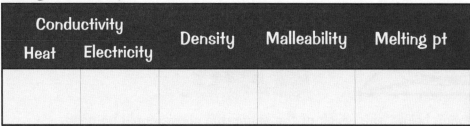

| Conductivity | | Density | Malleability | Melting pt |
Heat	Electricity			

  b) It was found that element Y formed 2 ions, Y^+ and Y^{2+}, so it can be used to make a variety of compounds. _Write down_ the formulae of the following compounds for the element Y: i) Y(I) chloride   ii) Y(I) oxide   iii) Y(II) oxide

Transition Elements and Alloys

12) Most of the transition elements are used to form alloys to improve their physical or chemical properties or to combine useful properties.

  What do you think the following alloys could be _used_ for?
  a) Titanium alloy _(light, strong and resistant to corrosion)_?
  b) Iron in the form of stainless steel: 70% iron, 20% chromium, 10% nickel _(hard and does not rust)_?
  c) Bronze: 90% copper, 10% tin _(harder than just pure copper)_?

13) It is possible to change copper sulphate crystals from blue to white.
  a) What substance are you _removing_ by turning them into white crystals?
  b) _How_ could you remove this substance?
  c) What would you _call_ this white powdered form of copper sulphate?
  d) The white powder will return to a blue colour if the removed substance is replaced.
    Give a laboratory _use_ for this reaction.

Transition Metals as Catalysts

14) The transition elements and some of their compounds make good catalysts.
  a) What is a _catalyst_?
  b) Match up each transition element _catalyst_ to its _function_:

A) Nickel	1) Haber process
B) Iron	2) Decomposition of hydrogen peroxide
C) Manganese(IV) oxide	3) Turning oils into fats

Top Tip   _Catalysts_ with _colourful compounds_ — that about sums up _transition_ metals. There's really not much more you need to know. They mainly vary in their _inner_ electrons only — so they're all pretty _similar chemically_. But make sure you know a couple of _examples_ of catalyst reactions — and can name uses for _iron, copper_ and _zinc_.

Rates of Reaction

Measuring Rate of Reaction

1) *Place* these chemical reactions *in order* of their speed, starting with the fastest reaction:

| Frying an egg | Striking a match | A car rusting | Concrete setting | Digesting food |

2) *When measuring the rate of a chemical reaction you can measure either the disappearance of reactant or the production of the product. Look at the apparatus below:*

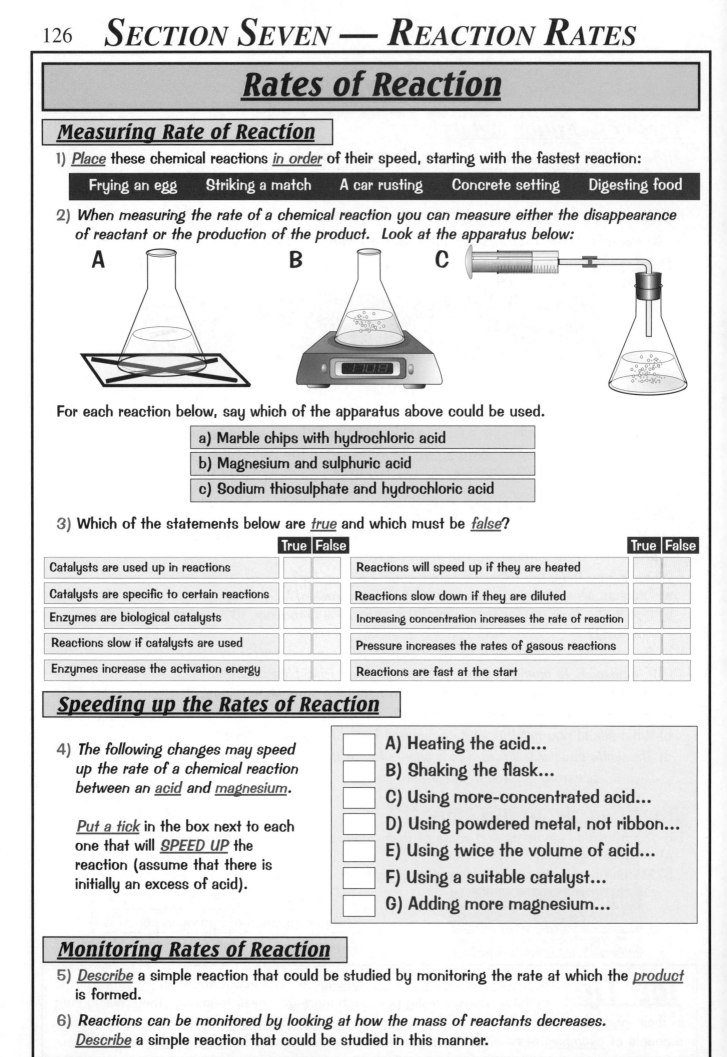

A   **B**   **C**

For each reaction below, say which of the apparatus above could be used.

| a) Marble chips with hydrochloric acid |
| b) Magnesium and sulphuric acid |
| c) Sodium thiosulphate and hydrochloric acid |

3) Which of the statements below are *true* and which must be *false*?

	True	False		True	False
Catalysts are used up in reactions			Reactions will speed up if they are heated		
Catalysts are specific to certain reactions			Reactions slow down if they are diluted		
Enzymes are biological catalysts			Increasing concentration increases the rate of reaction		
Reactions slow if catalysts are used			Pressure increases the rates of gasous reactions		
Enzymes increase the activation energy			Reactions are fast at the start		

Speeding up the Rates of Reaction

4) *The following changes may speed up the rate of a chemical reaction between an* acid *and* magnesium.

Put a tick in the box next to each one that will *SPEED UP* the reaction (assume that there is initially an excess of acid).

| | A) Heating the acid...
| | B) Shaking the flask...
| | C) Using more-concentrated acid...
| | D) Using powdered metal, not ribbon...
| | E) Using twice the volume of acid...
| | F) Using a suitable catalyst...
| | G) Adding more magnesium...

Monitoring Rates of Reaction

5) *Describe* a simple reaction that could be studied by monitoring the rate at which the *product* is formed.

6) *Reactions can be monitored by looking at how the mass of reactants decreases. Describe* a simple reaction that could be studied in this manner.

Rates of Reaction

Some More Questions on Rates of Reaction

7) Products are produced at a rate shown by a rate curve.
   a) On the axes opposite *draw* a *typical rate curve*.
   b) Place on the *curve* the following labels
      concerning the reaction rate:

   (A) FAST
   (B) SLOWING
   (C) STOPPED

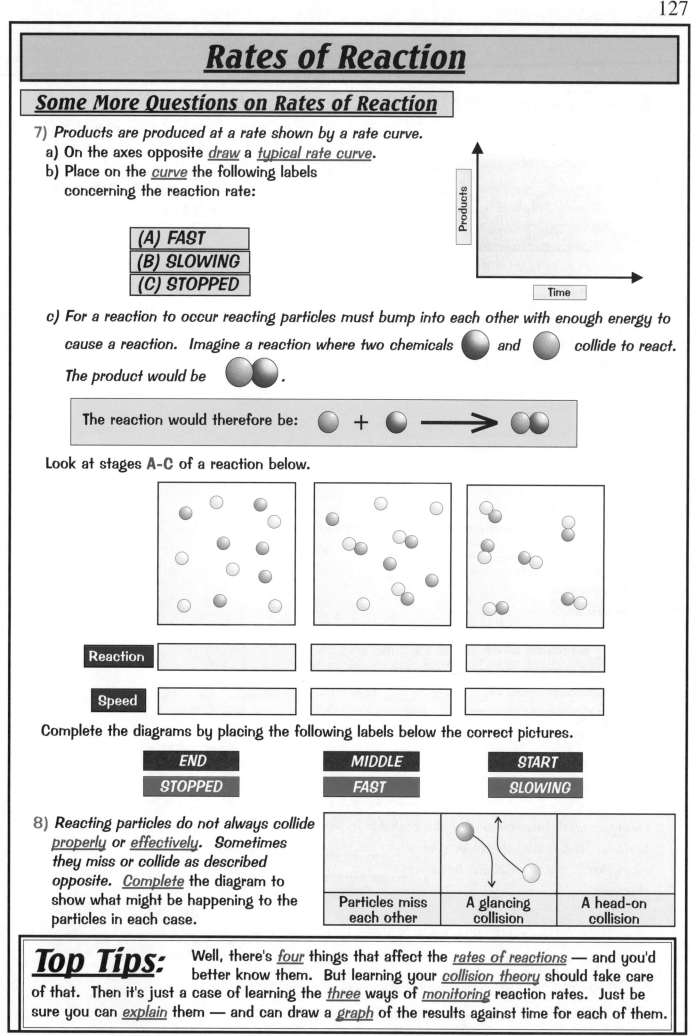

c) For a reaction to occur reacting particles must bump into each other with enough energy to cause a reaction. Imagine a reaction where two chemicals and collide to react.
The product would be .

The reaction would therefore be: + ⟶

Look at stages **A-C** of a reaction below.

| Reaction | | | |
| Speed | | | |

Complete the diagrams by placing the following labels below the correct pictures.

| END | MIDDLE | START |
| STOPPED | FAST | SLOWING |

8) Reacting particles do not always collide *properly* or *effectively*. Sometimes they miss or collide as described opposite. *Complete* the diagram to show what might be happening to the particles in each case.

| Particles miss each other | A glancing collision | A head-on collision |

Top Tips:
Well, there's *four* things that affect the *rates of reactions* — and you'd better know them. But learning your *collision theory* should take care of that. Then it's just a case of learning the *three* ways of *monitoring* reaction rates. Just be sure you can *explain* them — and can draw a *graph* of the results against time for each of them.

Collision Theory

The Four Factors that Effect the Rate of Reaction

1) Use your knowledge of reaction rates to *fill in* the blanks below. Then put the correct labels on the diagrams.

Fill the blank words (use more than once)
moderate   surface area   faster   collide   particles
catalyst   collision theory   concentration   energy
more often   successful   collision

Diagram labels
FAST   SLOW   HIGH CONCENTRATION
LOW CONCENTRATION   LARGE
SURFACE AREA   CATALYST PRESENT

Particles can only react if they _____ with enough _____ for the reaction to take place. This is called the _____ _____. There are four factors that can change the rate of a chemical reaction; temperature, _____, surface area and the use of a suitable _____.

Temperature

Increasing the temperature will cause the particles to move _____, with more energy. They will therefore collide _____ _____and with greater _____. These two things mean there are more successful collisions per second and therefore a _____ rate of reaction.

Concentration

Increasing the concentration of a reactant simply means there are more _____ which may collide and so react. More collisions means a _____ reaction.

Surface Area

Using a powder instead of a lump means the _____ _____ is greater, which means a greater area of reactant is exposed and so available for a collision. More collisions means a _____ reaction.

Catalysts

Use of a suitable catalyst means that the particles may react even if they collide with only _____ energy. This means more _____ collisions are likely. Some catalysts work because one of the particles is fixed to a surface. This makes the chance of a _____ more likely. More collisions means a _____ reaction.

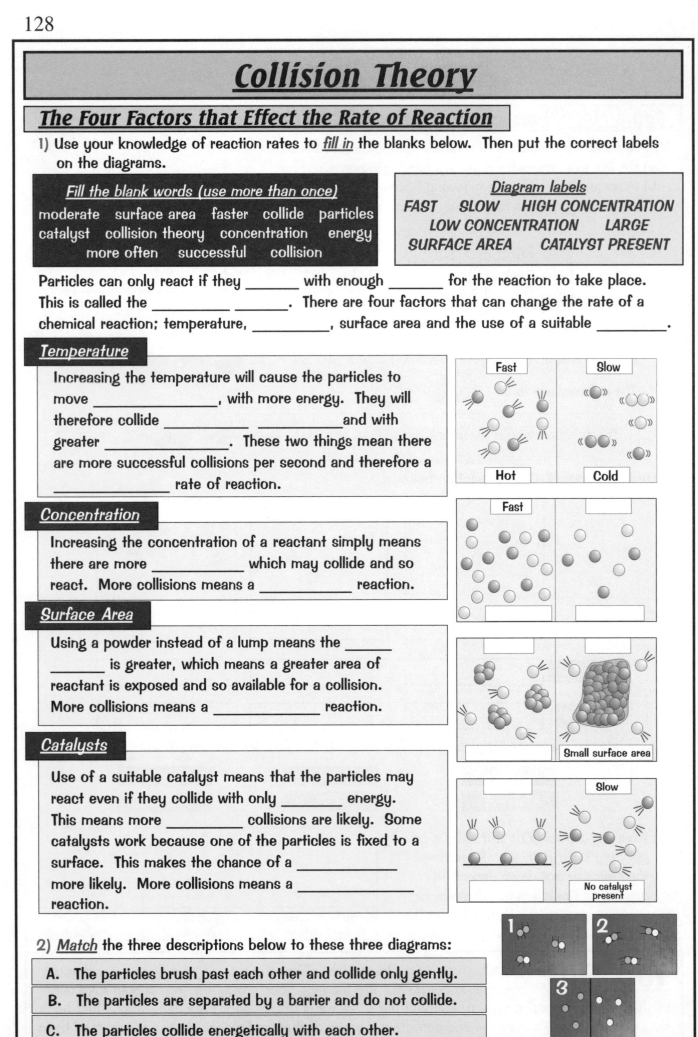

2) *Match* the three descriptions below to these three diagrams:

A.	The particles brush past each other and collide only gently.
B.	The particles are separated by a barrier and do not collide.
C.	The particles collide energetically with each other.

SECTION SEVEN — REACTION RATES

Collision Theory

Collisions of Particles

3) *Choose the sentence* that *best describes* the collision theory:

   a) Particles collide at random and always react.

   b) Collisions between particles often result in a reaction.

   c) Reacting particles must collide with enough energy in order to react.

   d) Collisions between molecules are sometimes needed before a reaction occurs.

4) *Four factors may have an effect on the rate of reaction.* *Match* each one with the explanation of how it works.

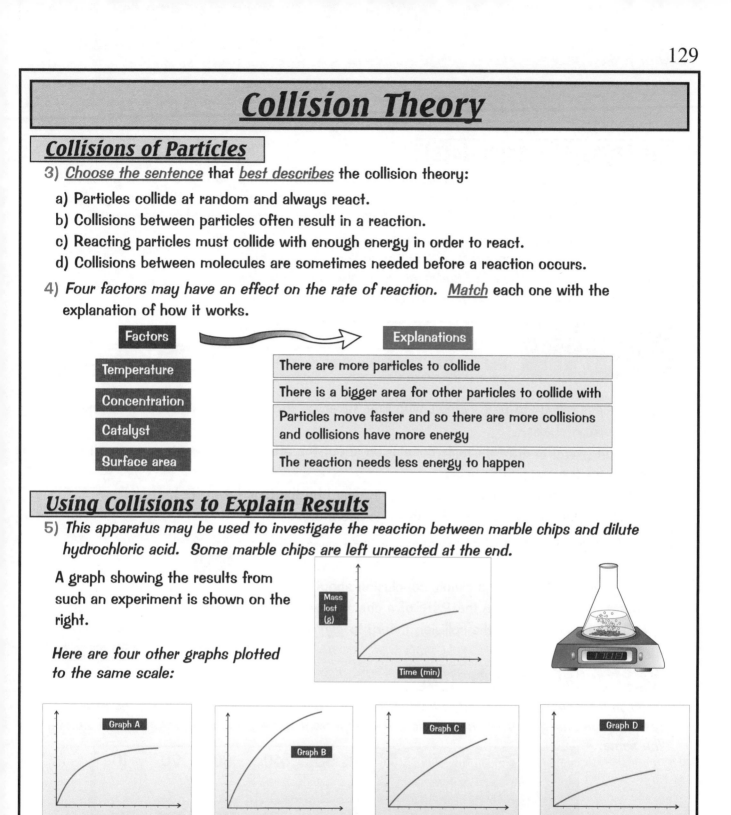

Factors	Explanations
Temperature	There are more particles to collide
Concentration	There is a bigger area for other particles to collide with
Catalyst	Particles move faster and so there are more collisions and collisions have more energy
Surface area	The reaction needs less energy to happen

Using Collisions to Explain Results

5) *This apparatus may be used to investigate the reaction between marble chips and dilute hydrochloric acid. Some marble chips are left unreacted at the end.*

A graph showing the results from such an experiment is shown on the right.

Mass lost (g) — Time (min)

Here are four other graphs plotted to the same scale:

Graph A   Graph B   Graph C   Graph D

   a) Referring to the original graph, *match each* of the graphs **A-D** with the correct description:

     i) the same volume of acid but twice as concentrated.

     ii) the same concentration of acid but twice the volume.

     iii) the same mass of marble chips but smaller chips.

     iv) the same volume and concentration of ice-cold acid.

   b) Use the theory of collisions to explain each of your answers to parts i) → iv).

Top Tips:
This collision theory stuff is what I call *real* science — it actually *explains* something — and makes all those reaction rates easier to remember.
And it makes sense — things only *react* if they collide at a suitable angle and with enough speed — so anything that increases their *speed* or *number of collisions* will increase the rate. Make sure you know how it applies to *temperature*, *concentration*, *surface area* and *catalysts*.

Experiments on Rates of Reaction

The Effect of Temperature

1) *The reaction between sodium thiosulphate and hydrochloric acid produces a yellow precipitate of solid sulphur. This makes the solution cloudy and prevents us seeing clearly through it. The cross below the flask in the diagram will slowly disappear as the sulphur is produced.*

In an experiment to investigate rates of reaction, the time taken for the cross to disappear was recorded. 50cm³ of sodium thiosulphate solution was used and 10cm³ of hydrochloric acid was added. The experiment was repeated at different temperatures.

Temperature (°C)	20	30	40	50	60	70
Time taken (s)	163	87	43	23	11	5

a) Use these results to *plot a graph*, with time taken on the vertical axis and temperature on the horizontal axis.

b) *Use the graph* to draw a simple conclusion about the effect of temperature on the time taken for the reaction to finish.

c) The rate of a reaction may be found by dividing 1 by the time taken (1/t). *Work out* the rate at each of the above temperatures.

d) *Plot a graph* of rate against temperature *(If the actual numbers for the rate value are too small to plot, use 'Rate x 1000' on the vertical axis).*

e) *Use your graph* to draw a simple conclusion about the effect of temperature on the *RATE* of a chemical reaction.

f) Use your knowledge of the collision theory to *explain* your conclusion.

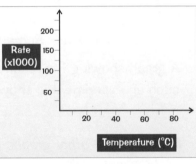

The Effect of Concentration

2) *The same reaction can be used to investigate the effect of* <u>CONCENTRATION</u> *on the rate of a reaction. In changing the concentration, it is important to keep the total volume used exactly the same.*

Volume of sodium thiosulphate (cm³)	50	40	30	20	10
Volume of water (cm³)	0				
Time taken (s)	80	101	137	162	191
Rate (1/t)					

a) *Complete* the table, adding the volume of water and calculating the rate of the reaction.

b) *Plot graphs* showing the time taken against volume of sodium thiosulphate used, and also rate against volume of sodium thiosulphate used.

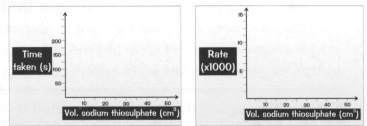

c) Use these graphs to draw a *simple conclusion* about the effect of concentration on the reaction rate.

d) *Explain* your conclusion in terms of particles and the collision theory.

Experiments on Rates of Reaction

A Question of Concentration

3) When magnesium reacts with acid, hydrogen gas is given off. This can be collected and measured as a way of measuring the rate of the reaction.

In this experiment 25cm³ of dilute hydrochloric acid (0.5mol/dm³) was reacted with a small amount of magnesium ribbon (the acid was in excess).

a) Write a _balanced equation_ for this reaction. (Mg + HCl → etc.)

b) Use the results below to _plot a graph_ of volume collected (vertical axis) against time (horizontal axis).

Time (s)	0	10	20	30	40	50	60	70	80	90	100
Vol. hydrogen (cm³)	0	9	18	27	36	44	50	54	56	57	57

c) _Mark_ on your graph where the reaction is going at a constant rate.

d) _How much_ hydrogen was collected in the first 25 seconds?

e) _How long_ did it take to collect 40cm³ of hydrogen?

f) _Sketch_ on the _same axis_ the graphs you would expect if the experiment was repeated using 25cm³ of:

     1.0 mol/dm³ acid .... mark this A.

     2.0 mol/dm³ acid .... mark this B.

     0.25 mol/dm³ acid .... mark this C.

A Question of Temperature

4) A similar experiment can be carried out to investigate the effect of changing the temperature on the rate of reaction. The graph below shows results from such an experiment. The acid is increasingly warmer in experiments 1, 2 and 3 .

a) What _simple conclusion_ can you draw from these graphs?

b) For each graph, _calculate_ the rate over the first 10 seconds.

c) What do you notice about the _change in the rate_ of the reaction for an increase of 10°C?

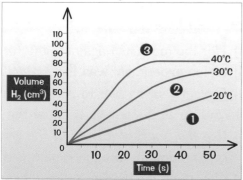

5) You are asked to investigate the effect of concentration on the rate of deposition of copper at the negative electrode in the electrolysis of copper sulphate solution.

a) _Draw_ a simple diagram of the apparatus you would use.

b) What factors would you keep the same?

c) Explain how would you _vary_ the concentration.

d) What would you measure?

Top Tips: Lots of graph-drawing practice here — and just as well, I'd say. Always make sure you've included a _title_, _axis labels_ and _units_ — and check the scale's about right. They'll look at all these in the Exam, and losing marks is so _easy_.

More on Rates of Reaction

Reactions that Lose Product

1) *Marble chips react with acid to produce carbon dioxide gas. This loss of gas means that the reaction can be followed by recording the mass every 30 seconds on a balance.*

The experiment was repeated using different sized pieces of marble:

Experiment 1 .... large chips
Experiment 2 .... small chips
Experiment 3 .... powdered marble

a) In carrying out this experiment, *what factors* must be kept constant?

b) Use the results in the tables to *work out* the total mass lost after every 30 seconds.

Experiment 1

Time (s)	Mass (g)	Mass Lost (g)
0	100	0
30	99.8	
60	99.6	
90	99.4	
120	99.2	
150	99.0	
180	98.8	
210	98.6	
240	98.45	
270	98.30	
300	98.20	
330	98.15	
360	98.15	

Experiment 2

Time (s)	Mass (g)	Mass Lost (g)
0	100	0
30	99.7	
60	99.4	
90	99.1	
120	98.8	
150	98.6	
180	98.4	
210	98.3	
240	98.2	
270	98.15	
300	98.15	
330	98.15	
360	98.15	

Experiment 3

Time (s)	Mass (g)	Mass Lost (g)
0	100	0
30	99.0	
60	98.5	
90	98.3	
120	98.2	
150	98.15	
180	98.15	
210	98.15	
240	98.15	
270	98.15	
300	98.15	
330	98.15	
360	98.15	

c) *Plot* the mass lost against time for all three experiments on the same axes.

d) Which experiment was the *fastest*?

e) *Explain* your answer to part d) in terms of particles and collisions.

f) Why do all the graphs finish at the *same point*?

g) *Use the gradient* (slope) of the graphs in the first 60 seconds to *calculate* the rate of the initial reaction for each experiment (*mass lost ÷ time*).

h) Why does the gradient — and hence the rate — *DECREASE* as the experiment goes on?

Everyday Examples

2) In terms of rates of reaction, *explain* these observations:

a) milk keeps longer if put in the fridge.

b) food lasts longer if stored in the freezer.

c) epoxy type glues need a *"hardener"* to make them work.

3) Give five everyday or industrial examples of each of these:

SLOW reactions (days or longer)	MODERATE reactions (hours / mins)	FAST reactions (seconds)

More on Rates of Reaction

The Use of Catalysts

4) The decomposition of hydrogen peroxide (H_2O_2) to water and oxygen is very slow. However, it may be speeded up by using a suitable catalyst.

Time (s)	Volume of oxygen collected (cm³)		
	MnO₂	CuO	Fe₂O₃
0	0	0	0
10	15	3	1
20	30	6	2
30	45	9	3
40	60	12	4
50	70	15	5
60	78	18	6
70	85	21	7
80	90	24	8
90	92	27	9
100	92	30	10

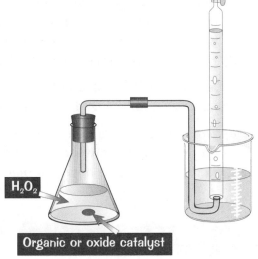

H₂O₂

Organic or oxide catalyst

Use these results to _plot three graphs_ on the same axes so that you can compare them easily.

a) Which _oxide_ is the best catalyst for this reaction?

b) Give a _reason_ for your answer.

c) What is a _catalyst_?

d) _Explain briefly_ how catalysts are thought to speed up reactions.

Living Catalysts

5) The breakdown of hydrogen peroxide may also be catalysed by enzymes in living cells, particularly those in liver and potato. Study the graphs below, which show typical results from such an experiment.

a) Which of potato and liver contains the most _effective_ enzymes?

b) Which _two graphs_ did you compare to answer (a)?

c) What is the apparent effect of _boiling the living tissue_?

d) Why is minced liver _more effective_ than the liver cube?

e) _Enzymes are biological catalysts._ State _three_ facts you know about enzymes.

f) _Give two_ everyday or industrial uses of enzymes.

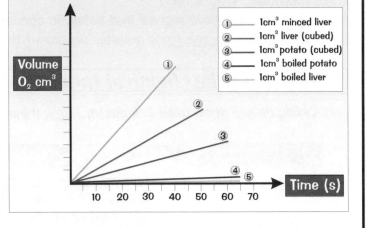

Top Tips: Ouch, yet more _graphs_ — but know your reaction rates and they won't hurt much. Just remember you can _lose marks_ in the Exam for _wonky points or lines_ — so get in the _habit_ of plotting things _carefully_. Simple really.

Catalysts

Questions on Catalysts

1) The diagrams to the right show how 0.5g of zinc and 0.5g of copper react with dilute sulphuric acid.

   a) Does the _copper metal_ react with dilute sulphuric acid?
   b) Does _zinc_ react with dilute sulphuric acid?
   c) How do _zinc and copper_ together react with dilute sulphuric acid?
   d) _Describe_ what copper does to the reaction in tube 3.

   > Tube 3 was left for several hours until the reaction was finished.
   > The copper was removed, dried and weighed. Its mass was 0.5g.

   e) What does this tell you about the _action_ of copper in speeding up the reaction between zinc and dilute sulphuric acid?

2) The graph shows an energy profile for a typical _exothermic_ reaction.

   a) _Mark_ on the graph:

   | the reactants | | the products | | the activation energy |

   | the energy change of the reaction |

   b) Use a different colour to mark the profile of the reaction when _catalysed_.

Cats and Cars

3) Catalytic converters are found in almost every new car. Their function is to clean up exhaust emissions and stop pollution.

   a) Name _three_ polluting gases found in "normal" car exhaust fumes.
   b) Into what _"harmless gases"_ are they converted?
   c) Why do all cars with a catalytic converter use _unleaded petrol_?
   d) The catalytic converter on any car is often less effective on short journeys. _Why_ is this?
   e) Some people have argued that catalytic converters do more harm than good. _Suggest one_ possible argument they might use.

Catalysts in the Chemical Industry

4) Catalysts are often used in industry. _Link_ these catalysts to the processes they catalyse:

CATALYST	PROCESS
Iron	Converting ammonia to NO whilst making nitric acid
Platinum	Contact Process to make sulphuric acid
Nickel	Making margarine from vegetable oils
Vanadium(V)	The Haber Process for the manufacture of ammonia

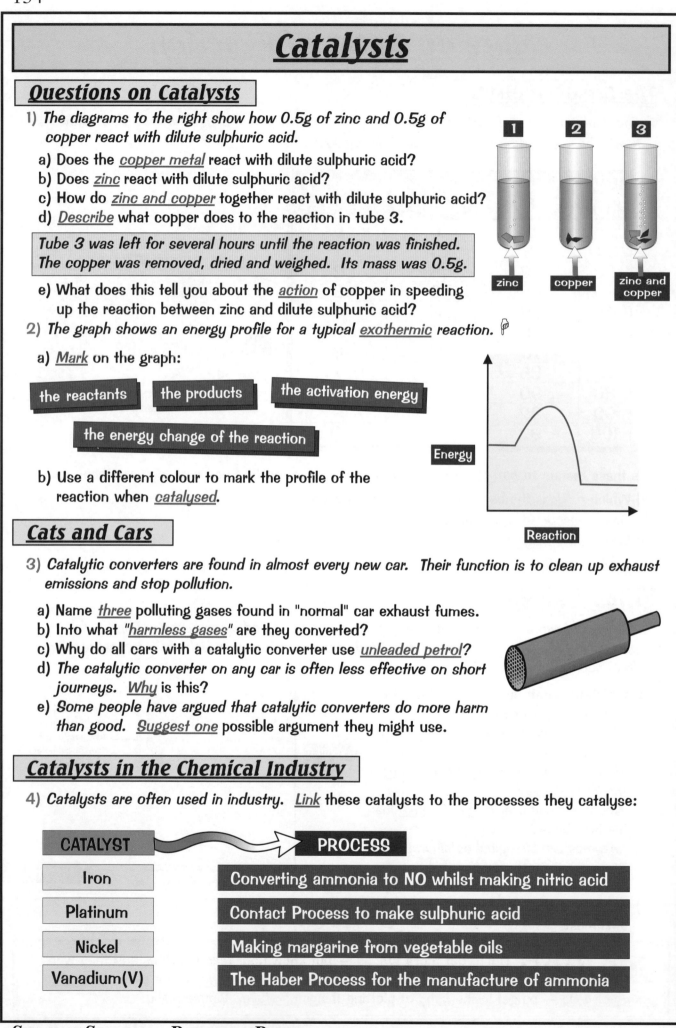

Catalysts

5) *The iron used in the manufacture of ammonia is often in the form of fine pellets. <u>Why</u> is the iron used in this form?*

6) What are the <u>advantages</u> of using catalysts in the industrial manufacture of chemicals?

7) Many industrial plants include a *"scrubber"* or *"cleaner"* in the plant before the catalyst. Why?

The Specific Nature of Catalysts

8) *The experiment shown can be used to investigate enzyme activity.*

Trypsin is an enzyme that catalyses the breakdown of protein. Photographic film has a protein layer that holds the silver compounds in place (these appear black). Different films use different proteins. If the protein is destroyed this black layer falls off leaving a clear plastic film.

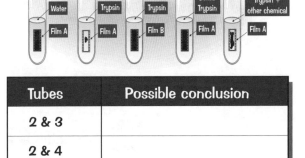

a) Look at the tubes carefully, then compare the pairs suggested, writing your <u>conclusion</u> in the table provided.

b) Why was <u>tube 1</u> included in the experiment?

Tubes	Possible conclusion
2 & 3	
2 & 4	
2 & 5	

9) *The ability of trypsin to break down protein depends on temperature. The experiment below investigates this. Strips of photographic film were each left for ten minutes in test tubes at the temperatures shown.*

a) From these results, what appears to be the <u>optimum temperature</u>?

b) Explain what happens to the enzyme at temperatures <u>above</u> the optimum temperature.

c) <u>Why</u> should trypsin have the particular optimum temperature demonstrated in this experiment?

Temperature: 20°C   25°C   30°C   35°C   40°C

10) *The browning of apples after being cut is an enzyme-catalysed reaction. An apple was cut into slices and left in different conditions.*

a) What <u>conclusion</u> can be drawn by comparing results 1 and 2?

b) What <u>conclusion</u> can be drawn from results 1 and 3?

c) What does <u>result 4</u> tell you about the nature of these catalysts?

In lab — 75% browning
Fridge — 40% browning
With lemon — Slightly less than 10% browning
Dipped in boiling water — Slightly less than 10% browning

Top Tips: The trickiest thing here is knowing how <u>activation energy</u> fits in — make sure you can <u>define</u> a <u>catalyst</u> in terms of it. Just don't forget how <u>specific</u> they are — and that they're <u>not used up</u> in reactions. Other than that, it's best to learn an <u>example</u> or two of how they're used in <u>industry</u> — a favourite Exam topic.

Enzymes

Simple Enzyme Questions

1) *Starch is converted to sugar by several enzymes:*

   a) Which enzymes are the best at converting starch to sugar?

   b) Why does trypsin, a common enzyme, not digest starch?

Enzyme	Percentage conversion after 30 minutes
Pepsin	0
Amylase	87
Trypsin	0
Maltase	67
Sucrase	42

2) *Unfortunately the head teacher spilled custard down his clean white shirt. A group of year 10 students offered to find the best way to get it clean. They cut up the shirt into squares and tested each with a different wash to find the best way to remove the stain.*

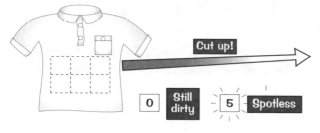

Treatment	How clean?
A) Hand wash in cold water	0
B) Warm wash with ordinary powder	3
C) 70°C wash with "Ace bio powder"	3
D) 40°C wash with "Ace bio powder"	5
E) Cold wash with "Ace bio powder"	3

   a) Which wash gave the *best result*?

   b) What is the special ingredient in "*bio*" or "*biological*" powders?

   c) Why did tests C and E not give a spotless result?

Cheesy Questions

3) *Cheese goes mouldy after a while.*

   a) What causes cheese and other foods to go off?

   b) Why does keeping cheese in the fridge help to keep it fresh for longer?

   c) *Explain* why meat or vegetables in the freezer stay fresh for months.

   d) Why must you use defrosted foods quickly?

4) *Loads of cream cakes were put in different places in the kitchen.*

   In which order should they be eaten if each is to be enjoyed as a *FRESH* cake?

Enzymes

Fermentation Reactions

5) The enzymes in yeast help to produce energy from sugar by breaking down glucose into carbon dioxide and ethanol.

a) Write a *balanced equation* for this reaction.

The experiment was repeated at different temperatures and the volume of CO_2 recorded every 30 minutes. The results are shown in the table opposite:

b) Use the results to *plot eight graphs* on the same axes. Set the axes out as below.

(For easy comparison, use different colours for each temperature).

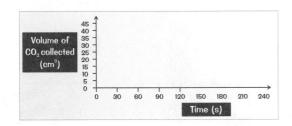

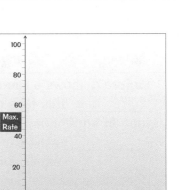

Time (s)	Volume of CO_2 collected (cm^3) at temperature (°C)							
	20	25	30	35	40	45	50	55
0	0	0	0	0	0	0	0	0
30	0	0	1	3	3	1	1	0
60	0	0	2	6	6	2	2	0
90	0	1	3	9	9	3	3	0
120	1	1	5	13	13	4	3	0
150	1	2	7	18	18	6	4	0
180	2	3	10	25	25	8	5	0
210	3	5	14	35	35	10	6	0
240	4	7	18	45	45	12	7	0

c) From your graphs, which temperature(s) appear to be the *best working temperature(s)* for this enzyme?

d) For each temperature, *calculate* the maximum rate of the fermentation (i.e. the steepest gradient).

e) Use these answers to *plot a graph* of rate against temperature, as shown on the right.

f) Use this graph to suggest the *optimum temperature* for this reaction.

g) *Explain* what happens to the enzyme at temperatures *above* this optimum temperature.

h) The process of fermentation is very important. *Name two* major products that depend on fermentation.

Use of Bacteria

6) Bacteria are used in the food industry as well as yeast.

a) Milk is the starting material for which *two* major foods?

b) Why is *pasteurised milk* normally used instead of fresh milk?

c) For one of the foods in your answer to a), *describe briefly* how it is made and the importance of the fermentation process.

Top Tips: *Catalysts* made of *protein* — that's all *enzymes* are. And it all depends on their *shape* — so the enzymes that catalyse the browning of apples *won't* make you any yoghurt. Learn one or two *examples*, and don't forget how *temperature* and *pH* affect their efficiency — make sure you can draw *graphs* of these.

SECTION SEVEN — REACTION RATES

Simple Reversible Reactions

Types of Equilibrium

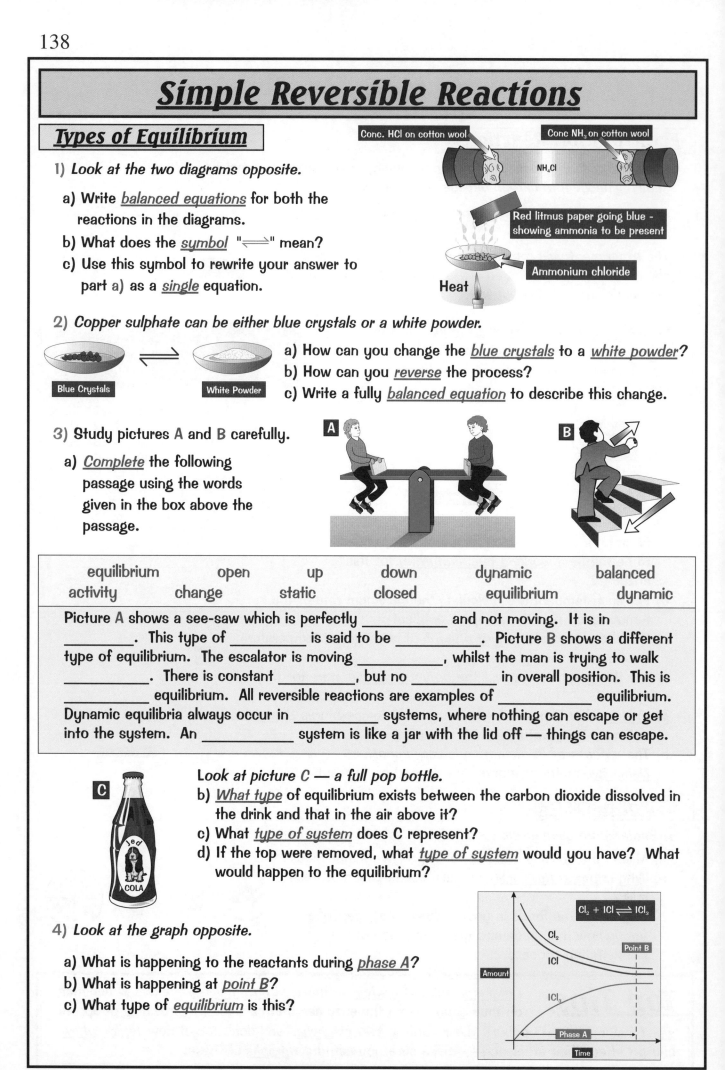

1) Look at the two diagrams opposite.

a) Write _balanced equations_ for both the reactions in the diagrams.

b) What does the _symbol_ "⇌" mean?

c) Use this symbol to rewrite your answer to part a) as a _single_ equation.

2) Copper sulphate can be either blue crystals or a white powder.

a) How can you change the _blue crystals_ to a _white powder_?

b) How can you _reverse_ the process?

c) Write a fully _balanced equation_ to describe this change.

3) Study pictures A and B carefully.

a) _Complete_ the following passage using the words given in the box above the passage.

equilibrium	open	up	down	dynamic	balanced
activity	change	static	closed	equilibrium	dynamic

Picture A shows a see-saw which is perfectly _____ and not moving. It is in _____. This type of _____ is said to be _____. Picture B shows a different type of equilibrium. The escalator is moving _____, whilst the man is trying to walk _____. There is constant _____, but no _____ in overall position. This is _____ equilibrium. All reversible reactions are examples of _____ equilibrium. Dynamic equilibria always occur in _____ systems, where nothing can escape or get into the system. An _____ system is like a jar with the lid off — things can escape.

Look at picture C — a full pop bottle.

b) _What type_ of equilibrium exists between the carbon dioxide dissolved in the drink and that in the air above it?

c) What _type of system_ does C represent?

d) If the top were removed, what _type of system_ would you have? What would happen to the equilibrium?

4) Look at the graph opposite.

a) What is happening to the reactants during _phase A_?

b) What is happening at _point B_?

c) What type of _equilibrium_ is this?

Simple Reversible Reactions

Changing the Position of Equilibrium

5) *Consider the reaction:* $N_2O_{4(g)} \rightleftharpoons 2NO_{2(g)}$ *ΔH is +ve (it's an endothermic reaction)*

Suggest what would happen to the equilibrium if you:
   a) increased the *temperature*.
   b) increased the *pressure*.
   c) doubled the *concentration* of N_2O_4.

6) The equation below shows the reaction occurring in the Haber process.

$N_2 + 3H_2 \rightleftharpoons 2NH_3$ *ΔH is -ve (it's an exothermic reaction)*

Suggest what would happen to the position of equilibrium if you:

   a) increased the *pressure*.
   b) increased the *temperature*.
   c) added more *nitrogen*.
   d) removed the *ammonia*.

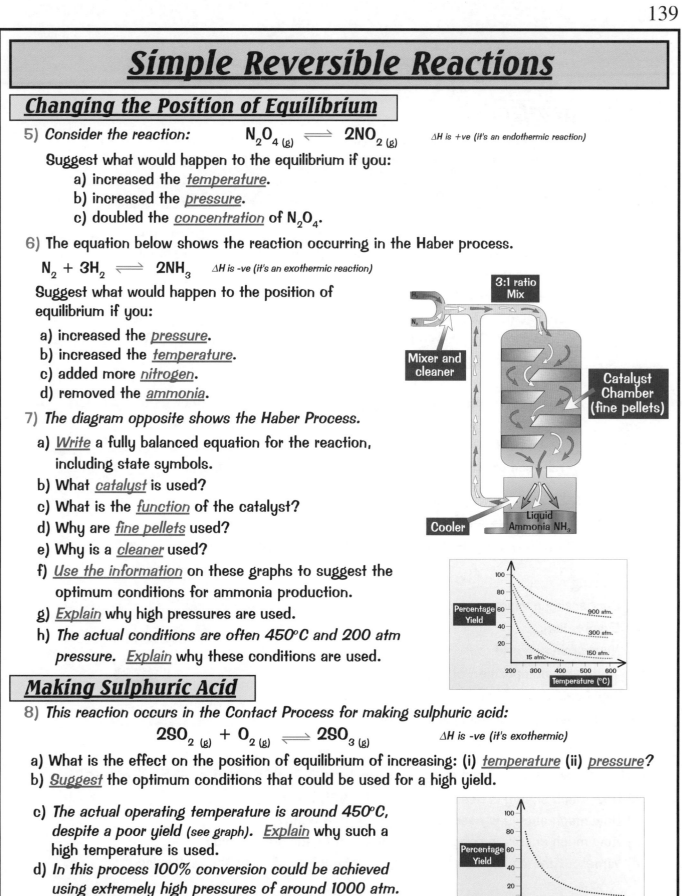

7) *The diagram opposite shows the Haber Process.*

   a) *Write* a fully balanced equation for the reaction, including state symbols.
   b) What *catalyst* is used?
   c) What is the *function* of the catalyst?
   d) Why are *fine pellets* used?
   e) Why is a *cleaner* used?
   f) *Use the information* on these graphs to suggest the optimum conditions for ammonia production.
   g) *Explain* why high pressures are used.
   h) *The actual conditions are often 450°C and 200 atm pressure. Explain why these conditions are used.*

Making Sulphuric Acid

8) *This reaction occurs in the Contact Process for making sulphuric acid:*

$2SO_{2(g)} + O_{2(g)} \rightleftharpoons 2SO_{3(g)}$ *ΔH is -ve (it's exothermic)*

a) What is the effect on the position of equilibrium of increasing: (i) *temperature* (ii) *pressure*?
b) *Suggest* the optimum conditions that could be used for a high yield.

c) *The actual operating temperature is around 450°C, despite a poor yield (see graph). Explain* why such a high temperature is used.
d) *In this process 100% conversion could be achieved using extremely high pressures of around 1000 atm. Suggest* a reason why this pressure is *not* used commercially.

Top Tips:
If two things can *combine*, then they can *separate* — so *any* reaction's basically reversible. Usually though one way's *much faster* than the other, so you don't notice. Make sure you understand *Le Chatelier's Principle* — if you can picture what's happening at the *molecular* level, you're much more likely to *remember* it.

Energy Transfer in Reactions

Energy Transfer

1) *Fill in the blanks* in the following passage (the words can be used more than once):

| energy | exothermic | endothermic | cold | taken in |
| hot | given out | negative | ΔH | energy | break | made |

A reaction that gives out _____ is called an _____ reaction.

A reaction that takes in _____ is called an _____ reaction.

_____ reactions can feel _____ as energy is_____ _____.

_____ reactions can feel _____ as energy is _____ _____.

The energy change of a reaction is often given the symbol _____. For _____ reactions the energy change is positive, i.e. heat is needed. A _____ energy change indicates an exothermic reaction, i.e. heat is released.

Virtually all chemical reactions involve _____ changes. Whether they are _____ or _____ depends on the balance between the _____ needed to _____ bonds in the reactant, and the _____released when bonds are_____ in the products.

Exothermic and Endothermic

2) *Classify these reactions* or changes as exothermic or endothermic:

a) Burning a fuel.

b) Condensing a vapour.

c) Evaporation.

d) Neutralising an acid.

e) Thermal decomposition of copper carbonate.

f) Rapid oxidation of iron.

g) Rapid dissolving of ammonium nitrate.

h)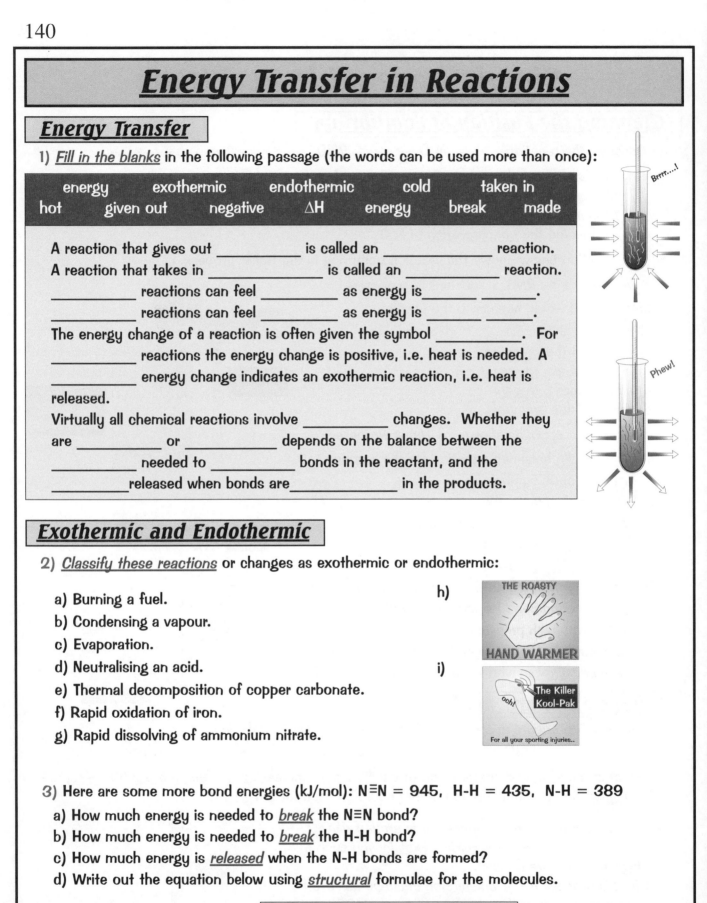
THE ROASTY
HAND WARMER

i)
The Killer
Kool-Pak
ooh!
For all your sporting injuries..

3) Here are some more bond energies (kJ/mol): N≡N = 945, H-H = 435, N-H = 389

a) How much energy is needed to *break* the N≡N bond?

b) How much energy is needed to *break* the H-H bond?

c) How much energy is *released* when the N-H bonds are formed?

d) Write out the equation below using *structural* formulae for the molecules.

$$N_{2 (g)} + 3H_{2 (g)} \rightleftharpoons 2NH_{3 (g)}$$

e) *Calculate* the energy needed to break all the reactant bonds.

f) Work out the *energy released* when the products are formed.

g) Hence calculate the *overall energy change* (i.e. *the net energy transfer*) for the reaction and *state* whether it is an *exothermic* or *endothermic* reaction.

Energy Transfer in Reactions

Breaking and Making Bonds

4) Burning ethanol can be represented by the following equation:

$$C_2H_5OH + 3O_2 \rightarrow 2CO_2 + 3H_2O$$

Bond energies (kJ/mol): C-C = 346, C-H = 413, C=O = 740, C-O = 360, O-H = 463, O=O = 497.

a) Write out the equation using _structural_ formulae for the molecules.

b) _Calculate_ the energy needed to break all the reactant bonds.

c) _Work out_ the energy released when all the product bonds are formed.

d) _Calculate_ the overall energy change, ΔH, and state clearly whether it is _positive_ or _negative_.

e) _State_ whether the reaction is _exothermic_ or _endothermic_.

5) Consider the reaction:

$$CH_4 + 2O_2 \rightarrow CO_2 + 2H_2O$$

Bond energies (kJ/mol): C-H = 413, O=O = 497, C=O = 740, O-H = 463

Given the above bond energies, _calculate_:

a) the total energy needed to _break all_ of the bonds of the reactants.

b) the total energy _released_ in making the bonds of the products.

c) the total _energy change_ (i.e. the _net energy transfer_) for this reaction.

d) Mark on the energy profile →

    i) The reactants ($CH_4 + 2O_2$).

    ii) The products ($CO_2 + 2H_2O$).

    iii) ΔH.

    iv) The activation energy.

h) Is this an _exothermic_ or _endothermic_ reaction?

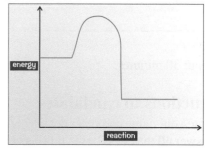

The Haber and Contact Processes

6) _Draw_ an energy profile diagram for the Haber Process.

7) In the _Contact Process_ for making sulphuric acid, sulphur dioxide is catalytically converted to sulphur trioxide:

$$2SO_{2\,(g)} + O_{2\,(g)} \rightleftharpoons 2SO_3$$

a) _Mark_ on the profile:

    i) The reactants.

    ii) The products.

    iii) ΔH.

    iv) The activation energy.

b) _Mark_ on the diagram the profile you would expect for a reaction catalysed by vanadium(V) oxide.

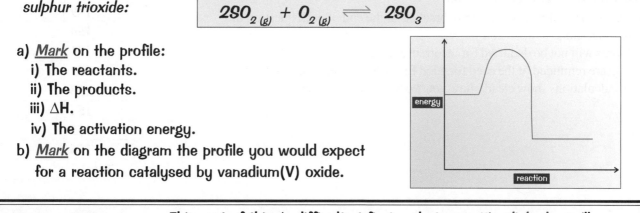

Top Tips: This sort of thing's difficult at first — but once it's _clicked_, you'll probably remember it. Just don't forget that pulling things apart _takes_ energy — so _breaking_ bonds is _endothermic_, while _making_ them is _exothermic_. Just make sure you can calculate the total energy _change_ of a reaction (ΔH) from _bond energies_.

General Certificate of Secondary Education

Science: Double Award
(Coordinated and Modular)
Higher Paper: Trial Examination

Monday 7 June 1999 9.30am — 11.00 am

Centre name								
Centre number					Candidate number			
Surname								
Other names								

(H)

In addition to this paper you will need a:
- Pen
- Pencil
- Calculator
- Ruler

Time
- 1 hour 30 minutes.

Instructions to candidates
- Write your name and other details in the spaces provided above.
- Answer **all** the questions in this paper.
- Write your answers in this combined question paper/answer book.
- Write your answers in blue or black ink or ballpoint pen.
- Do all rough work on the paper.

Information for candidates
- The number of marks is given in brackets at the end of each question or part-question.
- Marks will not be deducted for incorrect answers.
- You are reminded of the need for good English and clear presentation.
- In calculations show clearly how you work out your answers.

For examiner's use	
Page 143	
144	
145	
146	
147	
148	
149	
150	
151	
152	
153	
154	
155	
156	
Total	

1) The diagram shows the arrangement of particles in iron, water and air.

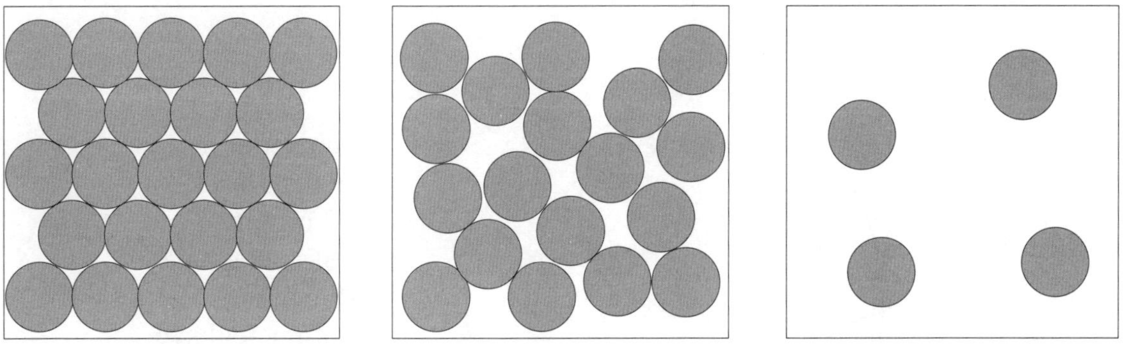

| Iron | Water | Air |

a) How can you tell that air is a gas?

....

....

....
(1 mark)

b) Air can be put into a bike tyre by using a hand pump.

Plunger

Explain why air can be easily squashed by the plunger.

....

....

....
(1 mark)

c) If the pump was filled with water and a finger placed over the end, why would it be difficult to squash?

....

....
(2 marks)

SECTION 8 — SCG EXAM

2) The structure of an atom of an element is shown below:

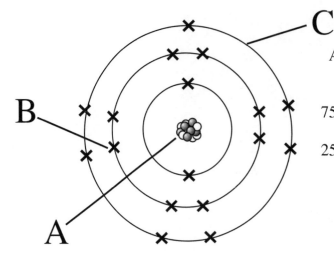

All nuclei of this element have 17 protons. 75% of nuclei have 18 neutrons. 25% of nuclei have 20 neutrons.

a) i) In which group of the Periodic Table would you find this element?

....

(1 mark)

ii) In which period of the Periodic Table would you find this element?

....

(1 mark)

iii) What is the mass number of this element?

....

(1 mark)

iv) What is the atomic number of this element?

....

(1 mark)

b) i) What do labels A, B and C represent?

A represents ....

B represents ....

C represents ....

(3 marks)

ii) What particles are found in A?

....

(1 mark)

iii) What charge would the most commonly formed ion of this element have?

....

(1 mark)

iv) What is the symbol for this element?

....

(1 mark)

SECTION 8 — SCG EXAM

3) Alkenes are unsaturated hydrocarbons and polymerise under certain conditions.

a) i) Draw out the displayed structural formula of ethene, C_2H_4.

(1mark)

ii) What does unsaturated mean?

....

....
(1 mark)

b) Alkenes are formed by the thermal decomposition of large hydrocarbons using a catalyst.

i) What name is given to this process?

....
(1 mark)

ii) How could you distinguish chemically between an alkene and an alkane?

....

....
(2 marks)

c) Addition polymerisation takes place when small alkene molecules join together to form saturated polymer molecules.

i) Complete the reaction below to show what happens when a propene polymerises.

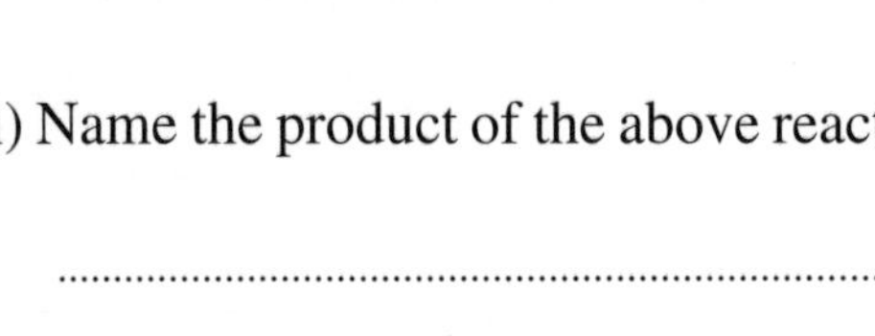

(1 mark)

ii) Name the product of the above reaction.

....
(1 mark)

iii) Give two uses of this polymer.

....

....
(2 marks)

146

4) Element Z has the following properties:

- It has a melting point of 708°C.
- It conducts electricity well.
- It conducts heat well.
- It forms giant structures with non-metals.
- It forms ions with charge 2+.

a) Is Z a metal or a non-metal?

....

(1 mark)

b) Is Z a solid, liquid or gas at room temperature and pressure?

....

(1 mark)

c) Which group is Z probably in?

....

(1 mark)

d) Ring the correct chloride formula:

ZCl ZCl_2 ZCl_3 Z_2Cl Z_3Cl

(1 mark)

e) Would the oxide of Z have a high or low melting point?

....

(1 mark)

f) Explain your answer to part e).

....

....

....

(2 marks)

5) The metals shown below were put in hydrochloric acid. The diagram shows what happened.

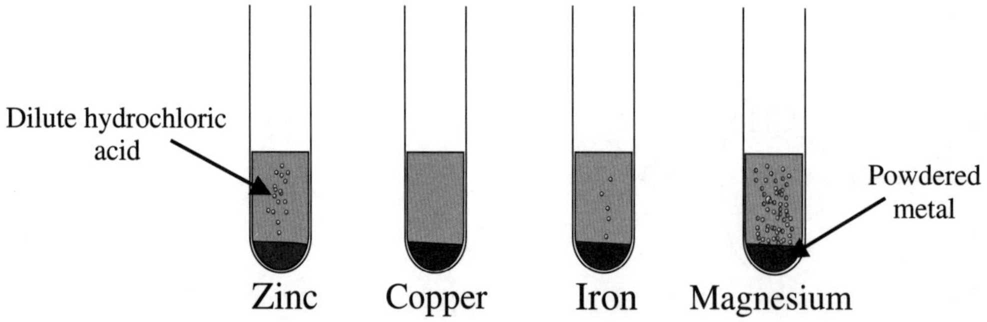

Dilute hydrochloric acid

Powdered metal

Zinc   Copper   Iron   Magnesium

Look at the diagram and place the metals in the order of their reactivity, with the most reactive at the top and the least reactive at the bottom.

Most reactive

....

....

....

....

Least reactive

(1 mark)

SECTION 8 — SCG EXAM

6) 10g of marble chips were placed into 100cm³ of 1m hydrochloric acid at 25°C. The gas produced was collected in a gas syringe over a period of time. The results are shown below.

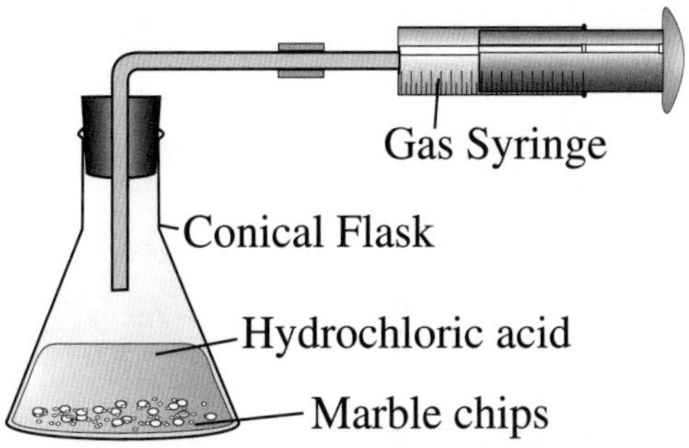

Gas Syringe

Conical Flask

Hydrochloric acid

Marble chips

Time/s	Volume of gas collected/cm³
30	10
60	20
90	29
120	41
150	45
180	47
210	47
240	47

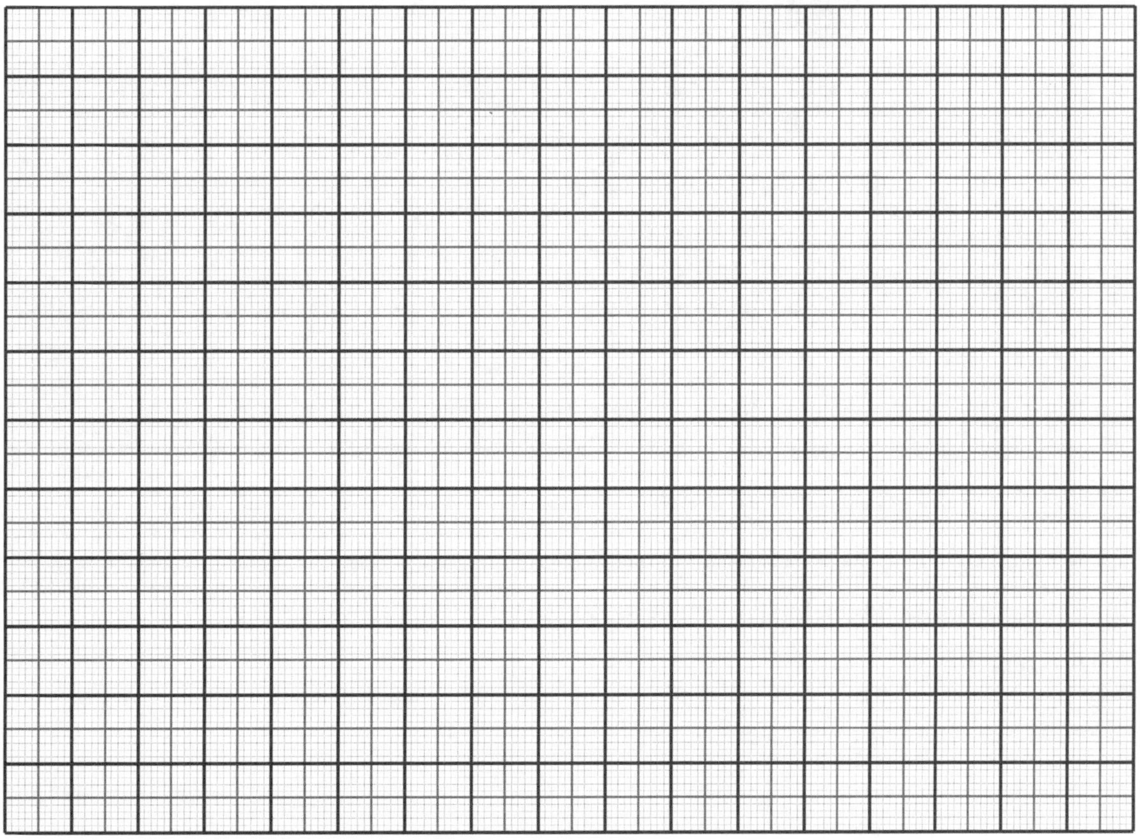

a) Draw a graph of the volume of carbon dioxide gas produced against time. *(4 marks)*

b) From the graph, at what time is the reaction the fastest: 90 seconds or 150 seconds?

....

(1 mark)

c) Explain how you worked out your answer to b).

....

....

(1 mark)

d) The reaction was repeated and was found to be faster when more concentrated acid was used. Explain, in as much detail as possible, why the reaction was quicker.

....

....

....

....

(3 marks)

SECTION 8 — SCG EXAM

7) The pie chart below shows some uses of aluminium.

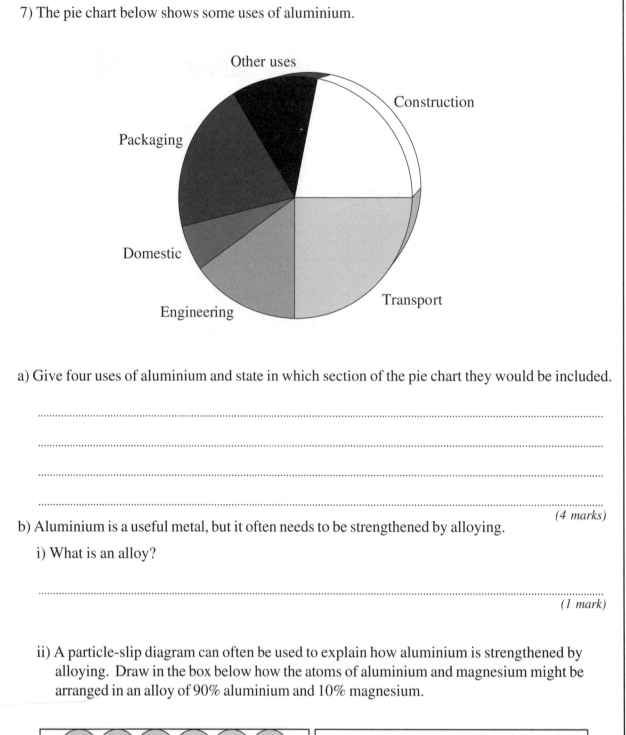

a) Give four uses of aluminium and state in which section of the pie chart they would be included.

....

....

....

....

(4 marks)

b) Aluminium is a useful metal, but it often needs to be strengthened by alloying.

i) What is an alloy?

....

(1 mark)

ii) A particle-slip diagram can often be used to explain how aluminium is strengthened by alloying. Draw in the box below how the atoms of aluminium and magnesium might be arranged in an alloy of 90% aluminium and 10% magnesium.

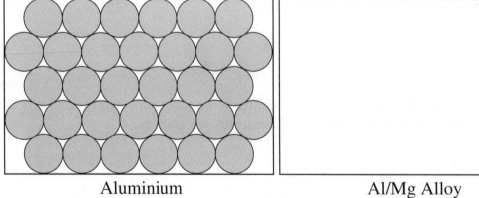

Aluminium   Al/Mg Alloy

(2 marks)

SECTION 8 — SCG EXAM

iii) The bar chart gives information about three metals.

Why is it important to recycle aluminium?

....

....

....

(1 mark)

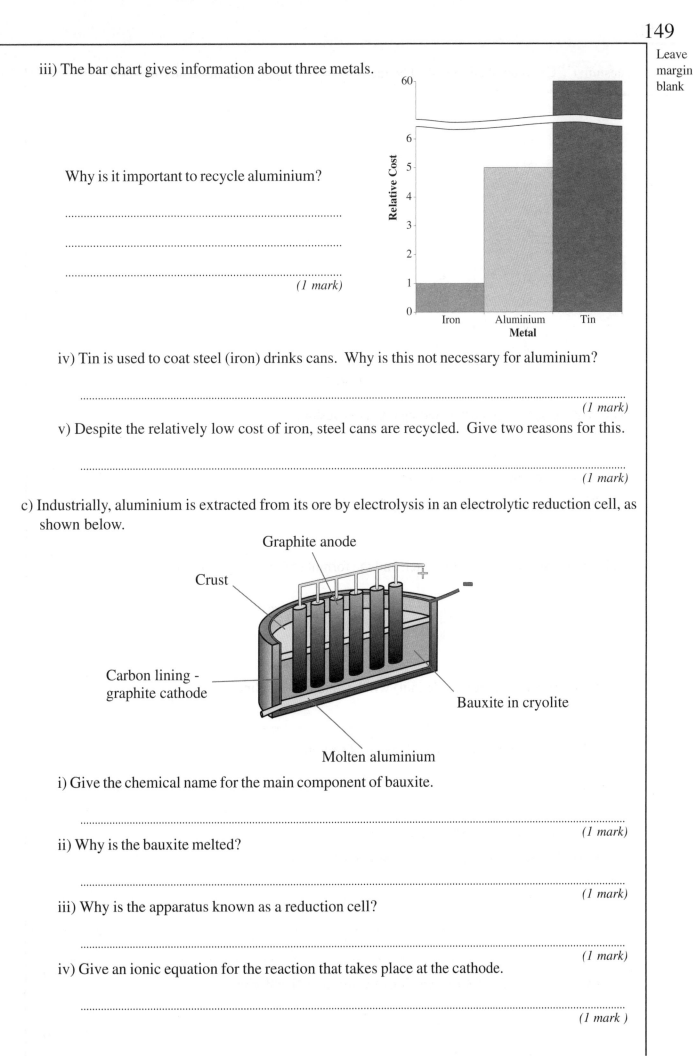

iv) Tin is used to coat steel (iron) drinks cans. Why is this not necessary for aluminium?

....

(1 mark)

v) Despite the relatively low cost of iron, steel cans are recycled. Give two reasons for this.

....

(1 mark)

c) Industrially, aluminium is extracted from its ore by electrolysis in an electrolytic reduction cell, as shown below.

i) Give the chemical name for the main component of bauxite.

....

(1 mark)

ii) Why is the bauxite melted?

....

(1 mark)

iii) Why is the apparatus known as a reduction cell?

....

(1 mark)

iv) Give an ionic equation for the reaction that takes place at the cathode.

....

(1 mark)

8) Caesium ($^{133}_{55}$Cs) is an alkali metal. The melting points of some alkali metals are shown below.

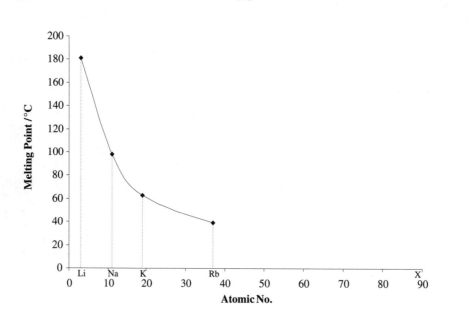

a) From the graph estimate the melting point of caesium.

....

(2 marks)

b) Predict the following about caesium:

   i) The charge on the most commonly formed ion of Cs.

....

(1 mark)

   ii) How caesium reacts with water, and the formula of the compound formed.

....

....

....

(3 marks)

   iii) Whether the solution made in ii) will be acidic or alkaline.

....

(1 mark)

   iv) Caesium's reactivity compared to that of sodium.

....

(1 mark)

c) Caesium forms a compound with chlorine.

   i) Describe how caesium can chemically bond to chlorine.

....

....

....

(2 marks)

   ii) Write an equation for the reaction of caesium with chlorine.

....

(2 marks)

SECTION 8 — SCG EXAM

9) The diagram shows a section through the Earth.

Give one difference between layers X and Y.

....

....

....

....
(2 marks)

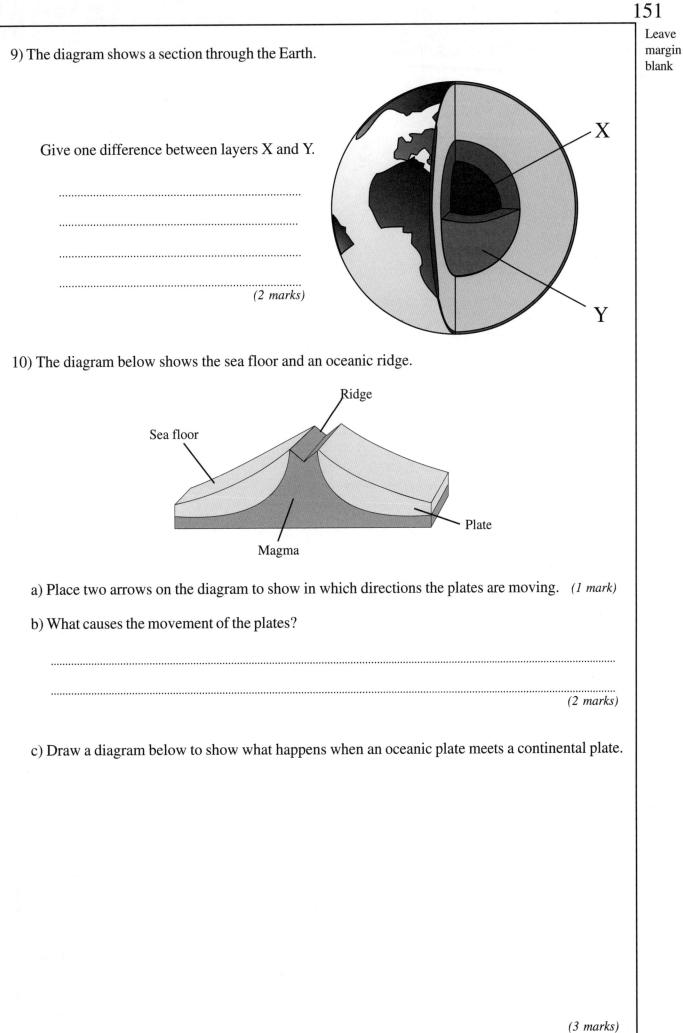

10) The diagram below shows the sea floor and an oceanic ridge.

a) Place two arrows on the diagram to show in which directions the plates are moving.   *(1 mark)*

b) What causes the movement of the plates?

....

....
(2 marks)

c) Draw a diagram below to show what happens when an oceanic plate meets a continental plate.

(3 marks)

SECTION 8 — SCG EXAM

11) a) Which one of the following diagrams best represents the structure of graphite?

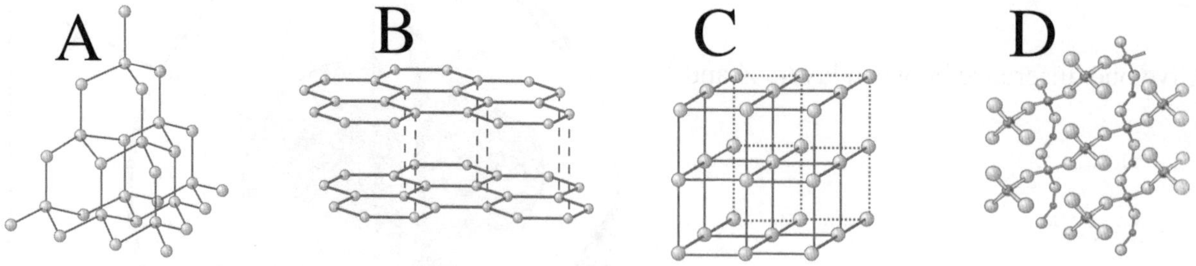

A   B   C   D

....

(1 mark)

b) Explain why graphite will conduct electricity.

....

....

(2 marks)

c) Why is it unusual that graphite will conduct electricity?

....

....

(2 marks)

d) Why is graphite often used as a lubricant?

....

....

(2 marks)

e) Sodium chloride is ionically bonded. List four properties that it will have because of its bonding.

....

....

....

(2 marks)

f) Explain one property given in e) in detail.

....

....

....

....

(2 marks)

SECTION 8 — SCG EXAM

) In the industrial production of sodium and chlorine, electricity is passed through molten sodium chloride, as shown below:

i) Write a balanced ionic equation to show the formation of sodium at the cathode.

....
(1 mark)

ii) Write a balanced ionic equation to show the formation of chlorine at the anode.

....
(1 mark)

h) A small amount of sodium was formed at the cathode by a current of 0.3 amperes flowing for 80 minutes.

i) Calculate the number of coulombs of electricity passed through the melt in this time.

....

....

....

Answer = ... coulombs.
(2 marks)

ii) Calculate the mass of sodium that formed at the cathode. (1 mole of electrons = 96,500 coulombs (1 faraday), A_r of sodium = 23.)

....

....

....

Answer = ... grams.
(2 marks)

[Turn over]

Section 8 — SCG Exam

12) Methane (natural gas) is used for heating and cooking in the home. When it burns it releases heat energy.

a) Give an alternative name for burning.

....
(1 mark)

b) What is the name given to a reaction in which energy is given out?

....
(1 mark)

c) Where in or around Britain might you find deposits of methane?

....
(1 mark)

d) Methane is a hydrocarbon. What is a hydrocarbon?

....
(1 mark)

e) Heat is produced when hydrocarbons burn completely. What chemicals are produced in this process?

....
(2 marks)

f) Incomplete combustion is when a chemical does not burn properly due to a limited supply of oxygen.

   i) What dangerous gas might be produced during the incomplete combustion of a hydrocarbon such as methane?

....
(1 mark)

   ii) Why is this gas particularly dangerous?

....
(1 mark)

SECTION 8 — SCG EXAM

3) Propane is used as bottle gas, as an alternative to methane in areas without mains gas supplies.

$$C_3H_8 + 5O_2 \longrightarrow 3CO_2 + 4H_2O$$

a) Use the diagram below to work out the energy released by the combustion of propane.

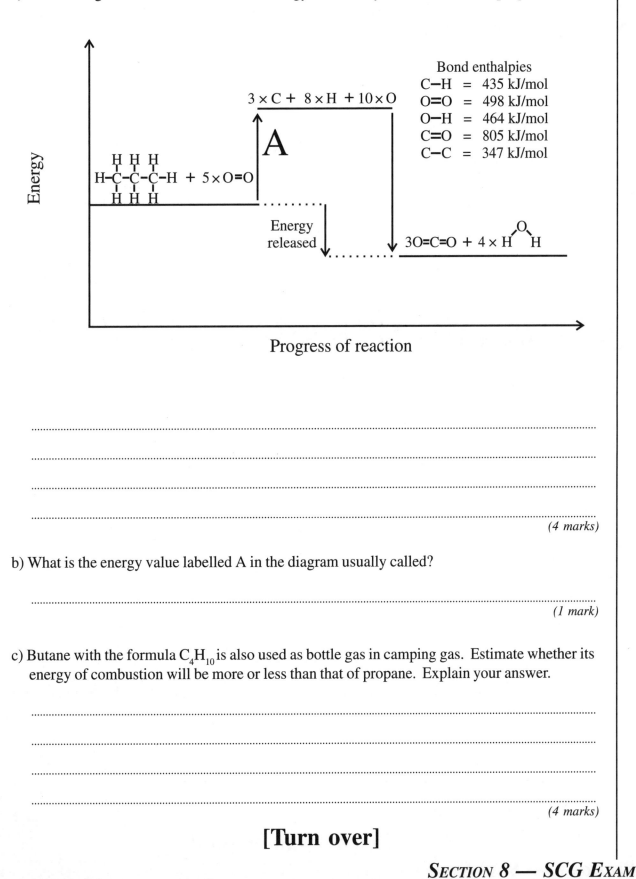

....

....

....

....

(4 marks)

b) What is the energy value labelled A in the diagram usually called?

....

(1 mark)

c) Butane with the formula C_4H_{10} is also used as bottle gas in camping gas. Estimate whether its energy of combustion will be more or less than that of propane. Explain your answer.

....

....

....

....

(4 marks)

[Turn over]

SECTION 8 — SCG EXAM

14) a) The graph shows the production of ammonia and fertiliser over the last few decades.

■ Ammonia is a pungent gas.
■ Ammonia is very soluble in water.
■ Ammonia is produced by the Haber Process.

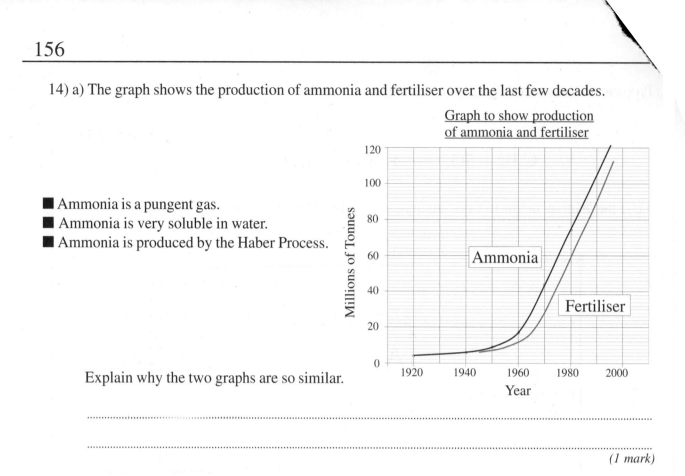

Graph to show production of ammonia and fertiliser

Explain why the two graphs are so similar.

....

....

(1 mark)

b) The table below shows the percentages by mass of nitrogen, phosphorus and potassium in three compounds that are used as fertilisers.

Compound	Formula	M_r	%N	%P	%K
Ammonia	NH_3	17	82	0	0
Ammonium Sulphate	$(NH_4)_2SO_4$	A	21	0	0
Ammonium Phosphate	$(NH_4)_3PO_4$	149	B	C	0

Calculate the missing figures A, B and C.

....

....

....

....

....

(6 marks)

c) Nitrogen is needed by plants as it promotes leaf and stalk growth.

Explain why ammonia is rarely used in this country on farm land, even though it would make a good fertiliser.

....

....

....

(2 marks)

[End of Examination]